SURVIVE IN FIVE LANGUAGES

Ceris Farnes

Edited by Jane Bingham and Rebecca Heddle

Illustrated by Ann Johns

Designed by Sue Grobecker

Language consultants: Anita Herbert, Christine Dowling, Valérie Zitoun, Marion Lorente Molto, Melanie Mauthner, Laura Leonor Salinas, Rosa Wroth, Liz Hamilton, Dott.ssa Mariella De Martini, Anke Kornmüller, Matthias Pflanz.

With thanks to The Lake School of English, Oxford.

Contents

About this book

This simple, up-to-date phrase book will help you to survive, travel and socialize in five European languages: English, French, Spanish, Italian and German.

How the book works

English words or phrases appear in the left hand column. The corresponding French, Spanish, Italian and German phrases are printed in separate columns across the page. The first letter of each language (e.g. F for French) appears at the top of each column.

Beneath each word or expression is a simple pronunciation guide for English speakers. You will find this helpful if you are not familiar with a particular language.

Newcomers to a language should look through the sections on pronunciation and how the language works at the end of the book.

Use the Contents list to find the section you need or look up words in the Index.

Familiar forms and slang

The words and expressions in this book are ones which you will find easy to use in everyday conversation. They range from the grammatically correct to the colloquial and from the polite to the casual. This depends on your situation and the person you are talking to.

Words are given in the form likely to be most useful. The level of politeness is pitched to suit each situation and casual forms are given as appropriate (for more about polite and familiar forms see "I, you, he, she, it etc." French: page 64, Spanish: page 67, Italian: page 72, German: page 75). If in doubt, use the polite form.

An asterisk (*) after a word shows that it is slang or familiar. Some common slang words and phrases are given on pages 54 and 55. Two asterisks (**) after a word show it can be quite rude, and it is safest not to use it unless you are very familiar with the person you are talking to.

Pronunciation

In the Italian pronunciation guide, stress marks (´) are used to indicate which part of a word should be given emphasis. The mark is placed in front of the stressed syllable, e.g. *oona bee-chee-´klet-ta (una bicicletta*, a bicycle).

In the French guide, brackets often appear around the letters r, m and n to show they are not pronounced clearly, but hinted at. The m and n are nasal sounds (see "French pronunciation" page 62).

In the German guide, brackets placed around the r at the end of a word show that it is pronounced like a short "a" (see "German pronunciation" page 74).

Masculine, feminine and neuter forms

Nouns in French, Spanish, and Italian are either masculine (m) or feminine (f). In German, they can also be neuter (n).

Many nouns and adjectives have a masculine and a feminine form. Usually, the masculine is given and the feminine ending is placed afterwards in brackets. If the (f) ending is added to the (m) word, a dash appears before the (f) ending in the brackets. If the (f) ending replaces the (m) ending no dash appears in the brackets. Occasionally, both forms are given in full: masculine/feminine.

Using languages

Always remember that you can make yourself clear in a foreign language with words that are not quite right or with very few words. Adding phrases like "excuse me" or "thank you" make anything sound more polite and generally guarantee a friendly response.

Absolute essentials

Useful phrases

	F	S
Do you speak English?	**Vous parlez anglais?**[1] *Voo par-leh o(n)-gleh?* **Tu parles anglais?**[2] *Tew parl o(n)-gleh?*	**¿Habla inglés?**[1] *¿A-bla een-glehs?* **¿Hablas inglés?**[2] *¿A-blas een-glehs?*
I don't understand.	**Je ne comprends pas.** *Je(r) ne(r) ko(m)-pro(n) pa.*	**No entiendo.** *Noh ehn-tyehn-doh.*
Can you say that again?	**Vous pouvez répéter ça?**[1] *Voo poo-veh reh-peh-teh sa?* **Tu peux répéter ça?**[2] *Tew pe(r) reh-peh-teh sa?*	**¿Puede repetir?**[1] *¿Pweh-deh reh-peh-teer?* **¿Puedes repetir?**[2] *¿Pweh-dehs reh-peh-teer?*

Helpful words

	F	S	I	G
hello	**bonjour** *bo(n)-joor*	**hola** *oh-la*	**salve** *'sal-veh*	**hallo** *ha-llo*
goodbye	**au revoir** *o re(r)-vwa(r)*	**adiós** *a-dyohs*	**arrivederci** *ar-ree-veh-'dehr-chee*	**auf Wiedersehen** *owf veeder-zayen*
hi	**salut** *sa-lew*	**hola** *oh-la*	**ciao** *chow*	**hi, hallo** *hi, hallo*
bye	**salut** *sa-lew*	**adiós** *a-dyohs*	**ciao** *chow*	**tschüs** *shewss*
good morning	**bonjour** *bo(n)-joor*	**buenos días** *bweh-nohs dee-as*	**buon giorno** *bwon 'jor-noh*	**guten Morgen** *goo-ten morgen*
good evening	**bonsoir** *bo(n)-swa(r)*	**buenas tardes** *bweh-nas tar-dehs*	**buona sera** *bwoh-na 'seh-ra*	**guten Abend** *goo-ten ah-bent*
good night	**bonne nuit** *bon-nwee*	**buenas noches** *bweh-nas noh-tchehs*	**buona notte** *bwoh-na 'not-teh*	**gute Nacht** *goo-te(r) nahkht*
Mr, Sir	**Monsieur** *me(r)-sye(r)*	**Señor** *seh-nyohr*	**Signor/Signore** *see-'nyohr/ see-'nyoh-reh*	**Herr** *hair*
Mrs, Madam	**Madame** *ma-dahm*	**Señora** *seh-nyoh-ra*	**Signora** *see-'nyoh-ra*	**Frau** *frow*
Miss	**Mademoiselle** *mad-mwa-zell*	**Señorita** *seh-nyoh-ree-ta*	**Signorina** *see-nyoh-'ree-na*	**Fräulein** *fro(r)-line*
yes	**oui** *oo-ee*	**sí** *see*	**sì** *see*	**ja** *yah*

I

Parla inglese?[1]
'Par-la eeng-'leh-zeh?
Parli inglese?[2]
'Par-lee eeng-'leh-zeh?

Non capisco.
Non ca- pee-scoh.

Può ripetere?[1]
Pwoh ree-'peh-teh-reh?
Puoi ripetere?[2]
Pwoy ree-'peh-teh-reh?

G

Sprechen Sie Englisch?[1]
Shprekhen zee english?
Sprichst du Englisch?[2]
Shprikhst doo english?

Ich verstehe das nicht.
Ikh fer-shtaye(r) dass nikht.

Können Sie das noch einmal sagen?[1]
Ku(r)nen zee dass nokh eyn-mal zahgen?
Kannst du das noch einmal sagen?[2]
Kanst doo dass nokh eyn-mal zahgen?

	F	S	I	G
no	**non** *no(n)*	**no** *noh*	**no** *noh*	**nein** *nine*
please	**s'il vous plaît**[1]**, s'il te plaît**[2] *seel-voo-pleh, seel-te(r)-pleh*	**por favor** *pohr fa-bohr*	**per favore** *pehr fa-'voh-reh*	**bitte** *bitte(r)*
thank you	**merci** *mair-see*	**gracias** *gra-thyas*	**grazie** *'gra-tsyeh*	**danke** *danke(r)*
excuse me	**pardon** *par-do(n)*	**perdone**[1]**/ perdona**[2] *pehr-doh-neh/ pehr-doh-na*	**mi scusi** *mee 'skoo-zee*	**entschuldigen Sie**[1]**, entschuldige**[2] *ent-shool-dikhen zee, ent-shool-dikhe(r)*
pardon?	**pardon?** *par-do(n)?*	**¿cómo? ¿qué?** *¿koh-moh? keh?*	**come?, scusi?** *'koh-meh?, 'skoo-zee?*	**wie bitte?** *vee bitte(r)?*
how much?	**combien?** *ko(m)-bya(n)?*	**¿cuánto?** *¿kwan-toh?*	**quanto?** *'kwan-toh?*	**wieviel?** *vee-feel?*

[1] Polite form. [2] Familiar form. See pages 63, 67, 71 and 75.

Asking the way

Getting help

	F
I'm lost	Je suis perdu(-e). *Je(r) swee pair-dew.*
Can you help me please?	Vous pouvez m'aider, s'il vous plaît? *Voo poo-veh meh-deh seel voo pleh?*
Where is the nearest ...?	Où se trouve le/la ... le/la plus proche? *Oo se(r) troov le(r)/la ... le(r)/la plew prosh?*
How do I get to ...?	Comment est-ce que je peux me rendre à ...? *Komo(n) ess-ke(r) je(r) pe(r) me(r) ro(n)-dr a ...?*
How far is it?	C'est loin? *Say lwa(n)?*
Can I reach it on foot?	Est-ce que je peux y aller à pied? *Esske(r) je(r) pe(r) ee alleh a pyeh?*
Can you show me on the map?	Vous pouvez me montrer sur la carte? *Voo poo-veh me(r) mo(n)-treh sewr la kart?*

Places to find

	F	S	I	G
railway station	la gare *la gar*	la estación de tren *la ehs-ta-thyon deh trehn*	la stazione ferroviaria *la sta-'tsyoh-neh fer-roh-'vya-rya*	der Bahnhof *derr bahn-hoaf*
underground station	la station de métro *la sta-syo(n) de(r) meh-tro*	la estación de metro *la ehs-ta-thyon deh meh-troh*	la stazione della metropolitana *la sta-'tsyoh-neh della metropol-ee-'ta-na*	die U-Bahn-Station *dee oo-bahn-shtatsee-own*
bus station	la gare routière *la gar root-yair*	la estación de autobuses *la ehs-ta-thyon deh a-oo-toh-boo-sehs*	la stazione degli autobus *la sta-'tsyoh-neh del-lyee 'ow-toh-boos*	der Busbahnhof *derr booss-bahn-hoaf*
hotel	l'hôtel *lo-tel*	el hotel *ehl oh-tehl*	l'albergo, l'hotel *lal-'behr-goh, loh-'tel*	das Hotel *dass hotel*
youth hostel	l'auberge de jeunesse *lo-bairj de(r) je(r)-ness*	el albergue de juventud *ehl al-behr-geh deh ghoo-behn-too*	l'ostello della gioventù *los-'tel-loh della joh-ven-'too*	die Jugendherberge *dee yoo-ghent-hairbearge(r)*
campsite	le camping *le(r) ko(m)-peen*	el camping *ehl kam-peen*	l'area di campeggio *'la-reh-a dee cam-'pej-joh*	der Camping-platz *der camping-plats*

S	I	G
Me he perdido. *Meh eh pehr-dee-doh.*	**Mi sono perso(a).** *Mee 'soh-noh 'pehr-soh/sa.*	**Ich habe mich verlaufen.** *Ikh hah-be(r) mikh fair-lowfen.*
¿Puede ayudarme, por favor? *¿Pweh-deh a-yoo-dar-meh pohr fa-bohr?*	**Mi può aiutare per favore?** *Mee pwoh a-yoo-'ta-reh pehr fa-'voh-reh?*	**Können Sie mir helfen, bitte?** *Ku(r)-nen zee meer hel-fen bitte(r)?*
¿Dónde está el/la ... más cercano(a)? *¿Dohn-deh ehs-tah ehl/la ... mas thehr-ka-noh/na?*	**Dov'è il/la ... più vicino(a)?** *'Doh-'veh eel/la ... pyoo vee-'chee-noh/na?*	**Wo ist der/die/das nächste ...?** *Vo isst derr/dee/dass nekhste(r) ...?*
¿Cómo se va a ...? *¿Koh-moh seh ba a ...?*	**Come si arriva a ...?** *'Koh-meh see ar-'ree-va a ...?*	**Wie komme ich zum/zur/nach ...?** *Vee kom-me(r) ikh tsoom/tsoor/nakh ...?*
¿A qué distancia está? *¿A keh dees-tan-thya ehs-ta?*	**Quanto dista?** *'Kwan-toh 'dee-sta?*	**Wie weit ist das?** *Vee vite isst dass?*
¿Se puede ir a pie? *¿Seh pweh-deh eer a pyeh?*	**Ci si arriva a piedi?** *Chee see ar-'ree-va a 'pyeh-dee?*	**Kann ich zu Fuß gehen?** *Kan ikh tsoo fooss gayen?*
¿Puede indicármelo en el mapa? *¿Pweh-deh een-dee-kar-meh-loh ehn ehl ma-pa?*	**Me lo può mostrare sulla cartina?** *Meh lo 'pwoh moh-'stra-reh 'sool-la kar-'tee-na?*	**Können Sie mir das auf dem Plan zeigen?** *Ku(r)-nen zee meer dass owf dem pla(r)n tsy-gen?*

	F	S	I	G
bank	**la banque** *la ba(n)k*	**el banco** *el ban-koh*	**la banca** *la 'ban-ca*	**die Bank** *dee bank*
post office	**la poste, les PTT** *la post, leh peh-teh-teh*	**la oficina de correos** *la oh-fee-thee-na deh koh-reh-ohs*	**l'ufficio postale** *loof-'fee-choh po-'sta-leh*	**die Post, das Postamt** *dee posst, dass posstamt*
telephone booth	**la cabine téléphonique** *la ka-been teh-leh-foneek*	**la cabina de teléfono** *la ka-bee-na deh teh-leh-foh-noh*	**la cabina telefonica** *la ka-'bee-na teh-leh-'foh-nee-ka*	**die Telefonzelle** *dee telefon-tselle(r)*
public toilet	**les toilettes publiques** *lay twa-let pew-bleek*	**los servicios públicos** *lohs sehr-bee-thyohs poo-blee-kohs*	**i gabinetti pubblici** *ee ga-bee-'net-tee 'poo-blee-chee*	**die öffentliche Toilette** *dee u(r)fentlikhe(r) twalette(r)*
supermarket	**le supermarché, le libre-service** *le(r) sew-pair-mar-sheh, le(r) leebr-sair-vees*	**el super, el supermercado** *el soo-pehr, el soo-pehr-mehr-ka-doh*	**il supermercato** *eel soo-pehr-mehr-'ka-toh*	**der Supermarkt** *derr super-markt*

Finding your way

Directions

	F	S
Follow the signs for...	Suivez les panneaux pour... *Swee-veh leh pa-no poor...*	Siga las señales para... *See-ga las seh-nya-lehs pa-ra...*
Take the first turn.	Prenez le premier tournant. *Pre(r)-neh le(r) pre(r)-myeh toor-no(n).*	Tuerza a la primera. *Twehr-tha a la pree-meh-ra.*
Go as far as...	Allez jusqu'à... *Alleh jews-ka...*	Vaya hasta... *ba-ya as-ta...*

Getting there

	F	S	I	G
When you get to...	Lorsque vous arrivez à... *lorske(r) voo-za-ree-veh a...*	Cuando llegue a... *kwan-doh lyeh-ga a...*	Quando arriva a... *'kwan-doh ar-'ree-va a...*	Wenn Sie zum/zur/nach... kommen *ven zee tsoom/tsoor/nakh... kommen*
on the right/left	sur la droite/gauche *sewr la drwat/go-sh*	a la derecha/izquierda *a la deh-reh-tcha/eeth-kyehr-da*	a destra/sinistra *a 'des-tra/see-'nee-stra*	auf der rechten/linken Seite *owf derr rekhten/linken tsyte(r)*
Turn...	Tournez... *Toor-neh...*	Gire.., Tuerza... *Ghee-reh...., Twehr-tha...*	Giri... *'Gee-ree...*	Biegen Sie ab nach... *Beegen zee ap nakh...*
Cross...	Traversez... *Tra-vair-seh...*	Cruce... *Kroo-theh...*	Attraversi... *At-tra-'vehr-see...*	Überqueren Sie... *Ewbe(r)-kvairen zee...*
Carry on...	Continuez... *Ko(n)-tee-new-eh...*	Siga... *See-ga...*	Continui... *Kon-'tee-nwee...*	Gehen Sie weiter... *Gayen zee vyte(r)...*
next to	à côté de *a ko-teh de(r)*	al lado de *al la-doh deh*	vicino a *vee-'chee-noh a*	neben *nayben*
just before	juste avant *jewst a-vo(n)*	justo antes *ghoos-toh an-tehs*	appena prima *ap-'peh-na 'pree-ma*	kurz vor *koorts for*
just after	juste après *jewst a-preh*	justo después *ghoos-toh des-pwehs*	subito dopo *'soo-bee-toh 'doh-poh*	kurz nach *koorts nakh*
opposite	en face de *o(n) fass de(r)*	enfrente de *ehn-frehn-teh deh*	di fronte *dee 'fron-teh*	gegenüber *gaygen-ewbe(r)*
the second	le/la deuxième *le(r)/la de(r)-zyem*	el/la segundo/a *ehl/la seh-goon-doh/da*	il/la secondo/a *eel/la seh-'kon-doh/da*	der/die/das zweite *derr/dee/dass tsvyte(r)*
the third	le/la troisième *le(r)/la trwa-zyem*	el/la tercero/a *ehl/la tehr-theh-roh/ra*	il/la terzo/a *eel/la 'tehr-tsoh/tsa*	der/die/das dritte *derr/dee/dass dritte(r)*

I	G
Segua le indicazioni per... *'Seh-gwa leh een-dee-ka-'tsyoh-nee-pehr...*	**Folgen Sie den Schildern zum/zur/nach...** *Fol-gen zee den shildern tsoom/tsoor/nahkh...*
Prenda la prima svolta. *'Pren-da la 'pree-ma 'svol-ta.*	**Nehmen Sie die erste Abbiegung.** *Naymen zee dee erste(r) ab-beegoong.*
Arrivi fino a... *Ar-'ree-vee 'fee-noh a...*	**Gehen Sie bis...** *Gayen zee biss...*

Look out for

	F	S	I	G
street	la rue, le boulevard *la rew, le(r) bool-var*	la calle *la ka-lyeh*	la strada *la 'stra-da*	die Straße *dee shtrasse(r)*
square	la place, le square *la plass, le(r) squar*	la plaza *la pla-tha*	la piazza *la 'pyat-tsa*	der Platz *derr plats*
subway	le passage souterrain *le(r) pa-sahj soo-teh-ra(n)*	el paso subterráneo *ehl pa-soh soo-teh-ra-neh-oh*	il sottopassaggio *eel sot-toh-pas-'saj-joh*	die Unterführung *dee oonter-fewroong*
roundabout	le rond-point *le(r) ron-pwa(n)*	la glorieta *la gloh-ryeh-ta*	la rotonda *la roh-'ton-da*	der Kreisverkehr *derr kryss-ferkair*
river	la rivière *la reev-yair*	el río *ehl ree-oh*	il fiume *eel' fyoo-meh*	der Fluß *derr flooss*
bridge	le pont *le(r) po(n)*	el puente *ehl pwen-teh*	il ponte *eel 'pon-teh*	die Brücke *dee brewke(r)*
traffic lights	les feux *leh fe(r)*	el semáforo *ehl seh-ma-foh-roh*	il semaforo *eel seh-'ma-foh-roh*	die Ampel *dee ampel*
crossroads	le carrefour *le(r) kar-foor*	el cruce *ehl kroo-theh*	l'incrocio *leen-'kroh-choh*	die Kreuzung *dee kroytsoong*
main road	la route principale *la root pra(n)-see-pal*	la carretera principal *la ka-reh-teh-ra preen-thee-pal*	la strada principale *la 'stra-da preen-chee-'pa-leh*	die Hauptstraße *dee howpt-shtrasse(r)*
motorway	l'autoroute *lo-to-root*	la autopista *la a-oo-toh-pees-ta*	l'autostrada *'low-tos-'tra-da*	die Autobahn *dee owtoe-bahn*
car park	le parking *le(r) par-keen*	el aparcamiento *ehl a-par-ka-myehn-toh*	il parcheggio *eel par-'kej-joh.*	der Parkplatz *derr park-plats*

Travel: by train and bus

Making enquiries

	F
When is the next train to...?	**A quelle heure est le prochain train pour...?** *A kellur eh le(r) prosha(n) tra(n) poor...?*
When is the last bus to...?	**A quelle heure part le dernier bus pour...?** *A kellur par le(r) dair-nyeh bews poor...?*
Do I have to change?	**Je dois changer?** *Je(r) dwa sho(n)-jeh?*

Buying a ticket

	F
Where can I buy a ticket?	**Où est-ce que je peux acheter un billet?** *Oo-esske(r) je(r) pe(r) ash-teh u(n) bee-yeh?*
I want to go to...	**Je voudrais aller à...** *Je(r) voo-dreh alleh a...*
Can I have a one way ticket to...?	**Est-ce que je peux avoir un aller simple pour...?** *Esske(r) je(r) pe(r) avwar-un alleh sa(m)pl poor...?*

Travel words

	F	S	I	G
bus station	la gare routière *la gahr roo-tyair*	la estación de autobuses *la ehs-ta-thyon deh a-oo-toh-boo-sehs*	la stazione degli autobus *la sta-'tsyoh-neh del-lyee ow-to-boos*	der Busbahnhof *derr booss-bahn-hoaf*
bus stop	l'arrêt d'autobus *larreh do-to-bews*	la parada de autobús *la pa-ra-da deh a-oo-toh-boos*	la fermata dell'autobus *la fehr-'ma-ta dell 'ow-toh-boos*	die Bushaltestelle *dee booss-halte(r)-shtelle(r)*
railway station	la gare *la gahr*	la estación de tren *la ehs-ta-thyon deh trehn*	la stazione ferroviaria *la sta-'tsyoh-neh fehr-roh-vya-rya*	der Bahnhof *derr bahn-hoaf*
underground station	la station de métro *la sta-syo(n) de(r) meh-tro*	la estación de metro *la ehs-ta-thyon deh meh-troh*	la stazione della metropolitana *la sta-'tsyoh-neh della metropol-ee-'ta-na*	die U-Bahn-Station *dee oo-bahn-shtatsee-own*
ticket office	le guichet *le(r) gee-sheh*	la taquilla de billetes *la ta-kee-lyah deh bee-lyeh-tehs*	la biglietteria *la beel-'lyet-teh-'ree-a*	der Fahrkarten-schalter *derr fahr-karten-shalter*

S	I	G
¿Cuándo sale el próximo tren para . . . ? *¿Kwan-doh sa-leh ehl prohx-ee-moh trehn pa-ra . . . ?*	**A che ora parte il prossimo treno per . . . ?** *A keh 'oh-ra par-teh eel 'pros-see-moh 'treh-no pehr. . . ?*	**Wann fährt der nächste Zug nach . . . ?** *Vann faht derr nekhste(r) tsook nakh . . . ?*
¿Cuándo sale el último autobús para . . . ? *¿Kwan-doh sa-leh ehl ool-tee-moh a-oo-toh-boos pa-ra . . . ?*	**A che ora è l'ultimo autobus per . . . ?** *A keh 'oh-ra eh 'lool-tee-moh 'ow-toh-boos pehr. . . ?*	**Wann fährt der letzte Bus nach . . . ?** *Vann faht derr letste(r) booss nakh . . . ?*
¿Tengo que hacer algún transbordo? *¿Tehn-goh keh a-thehr al-goon trans-bohr-doh?*	**Devo cambiare?** *'Deh-voh kam-byah-reh?*	**Muß ich umsteigen?** *Mooss ikh oom-shtygen?*

S	I	G
¿Dónde puedo comprar un billete? *¿Dohn-deh pweh-doh kohm-prar oon bee-lyeh-teh?*	**Dove si compra il biglietto?** *'Doh-veh see 'kom-pra eel bee-'lyet-toh?*	**Wo kann ich eine Fahrkarte kaufen?** *Vo kan ikh eyne(r) fahr-karte(r) kowfen?*
Quiero ir a . . . *Kyeh-roh eer a . . .*	**Devo andare a . . .** *'Deh-voh an-'da-reh a . . .*	**Ich möchte nach . . .** *Ikh mu(r)khte(r) nakh . . .*
Un billete de ida a . . . *Oon bee-lyeh-teh deh ee-da a . . .*	**Un biglietto di sola andata per . . .** *Oon beel-'lyet-toh dee 'soh-la an-'da-ta pehr. . .*	**Kann ich eine einfache Fahrkarte nach . . . haben?** *Kan ikh eyne(r) eynfakhe(r) fahr-karte(r) nakh . . . ha-ben?*

	F	S	I	G
a single	**un aller simple** *un alleh sa(m)pl*	**un billete de ida** *oon bee-lyeh-teh deh ee-da*	**un biglietto di sola andata** *oon beel-'lyet-toh dee 'soh-la an-da-ta*	**eine Einfach-karte** *eyne(r) eynfakh-karte(r)*
a return	**un aller et retour** *un alleh e(h) re(r)-toor*	**un billete de ida y vuelta** *oon bee-lyeh-teh deh ee-da ee bwehl-ta*	**un biglietto di andata e ritorno** *oon beel-'lyet-toh dee an-da-ta eh ree-'tor-no*	**eine Rückfahrkarte** *eyne(r) rewk-far-karte(r)*
student fare	**tarif étudiant** *ta-reef eh-tew-dyo(n)*	**tarifa de estudiante** *ta-ree-fa deh ehs-too-dyan-tehs*	**tariffa studenti** *ta-'reef-fa stoo-'den-tee*	**Studentener-mäßigung** *shtoodenten-air-messigoong*
youth fare	**tarif jeune** *ta-reef jurn*	**tarifa joven** *ta-ree-fa ghoh-behn*	**tariffa ridotta** *ta-reef-fa ree-'dot-ta*	**Fahrpreis für Jugendliche** *fahr-price fewr yoogentlikhe(r)*
timetable	**un horaire** *un orair*	**un horario** *oon oh-rar-yoh*	**un orario** *oon oh-'ra-ryoh*	**ein Fahrplan** *eyn fahr-plan*
platform	**le quai** *le(r) keh*	**el andén** *ehl an-dehn*	**il binario** *eel bee-'na-ryoh*	**der Bahnsteig** *derr bahn-shtike*

Travel: on the road

Taxis

	F
Where can I get a taxi?	Où est-ce que je peux prendre un taxi? *Oo esske(r) je(r) pe(r) pro(n)dr u(n) tax-ee?*
What's the fare to...?	C'est combien pour aller à...? *Say ko(m)bya(n) poor alleh a...?*
Stop here please.	Arrêtez vous ici s'il vous plait. *A-reh-teh voo ee-see seel voo pleh.*

Hiring

	F	S
Can I hire...?	Je voudrais louer... *Je(r) voo-dreh loo-eh...*	¿Alquilan...? *¿Al-kee-lan...?*
...for a day/a week.	...pour un jour/une semaine. *...poor u(n) joor/ewn se(r)-men.*	...por un día/una semana. *...pohr oon dee-a/oo-na seh-ma-na.*
How do the controls work?	Comment marchent les commandes? *Ko-mo(n) marsh leh ko-mo(n)d?*	¿Cómo funcionan los mandos? *¿Koh-moh foon-thyoh-nan lohs man-dohs?*

Travel words

	F	S	I	G
for hire	à louer *a loo-eh*	de alquiler *deh al-kee-lehr*	a noleggio *a noh-'lej-joh*	zu vermieten *tsoo fer-meeten*
car	une voiture *ewn vwa-tewr*	un coche *oon koh-tcheh*	una macchina, un'auto *oona 'mak-kee-na, oon 'ow-toh*	ein Auto *eyn owtoe*
bicycle	une bicyclette *ewn bee-see-klet*	una bicicleta *oo-na bee-thee-kleh-ta*	una bicicletta *oona bee-chee-'klet-ta*	ein Fahrrad *eyn far-rat*
moped	un vélomoteur *u(n) veh-lo-mo-tur*	una motocicleta *oo-na moh-toh-thee-kleh-ta*	un motorino *oon moh-toh-'ree-noh*	ein Moped *eyn mo-ped*
motorbike	une moto *ewn mo-to*	una moto *oo-na moh-toh*	una moto *oona 'moh-toh*	ein Motorrad *eyn moto-rat*
driving licence	un permis de conduire *u(n) pair-mee de(r) ko(n)-dweer*	un carnet de conducir *oon kar-neh deh kohn-doo-theer*	una patente di guida *oona pa-'ten-teh dee 'gwee-da*	ein Führerschein *eyn fewrer-shine*

S	I	G
¿Dónde puedo coger un taxi? *¿Dohn-deh pweh-doh koh-ghehr oon tax-ee?*	**Dove posso prendere un tassì?** *'Doh-veh pos-soh 'prehn-deh-reh oon 'tas-see?*	**Wo bekomme ich ein Taxi?** *Vo be-komme(r) ikh eyn taxi?*
¿Cuánto costaría ir a…? *¿Kwan-toh kohs-ta-ree-a eer a…?*	**Qual è la tariffa per…?** *Kwa-'leh la ta-'reef-fa pehr…?*	**Was kostet es zur…?** *Vass kostet ess tsoor…?*
Pare aquí, por favor. *Pa-reh a-kee, pohr fa-bohr.*	**Si fermi qui, prego.** *See 'fehr-mee kwee, 'preh-goh.*	**Halten Sie bitte hier an.** *Halten zee bitte(r) heer an.*

I	G
Posso noleggiare…? *'Pos-soh noh-lej-'ja-reh…?*	**Kann ich… mieten?** *Kan ikh… mee-ten?*
…per un giorno/una settimana. *…pehr oon 'jor-noh/oona set-tee-'ma-na.*	**…für einen Tag/eine Woche.** *…fewr eynen tak/eyne(r) vokhe(r).*
Come funzionano i comandi? *'Koh-meh foon-'tsyoh-na-noh ee koh-'man-dee?*	**Wie funktionieren die Schalter?** *Vee foonk-see-oneert dee shalter?*

	F	S	I	G
petrol station	**une station-service** *ewn sta-syon sair-vees*	**una gasolinera** *oo-na ga-soh-lee-neh-ra*	**un benzinaio** *oon ben-tsee-'na-yoh*	**eine Tankstelle** *eyne(r) tank-shtelle(r)*
petrol	**de l'essence** *de(r) lesso(n)s*	**la gasolina** *la ga-soh-lee-na*	**la benzina** *la ben-'tsee-na*	**das Benzin** *dass ben-zeen*
diesel	**du diesel** *dew dee-zel*	**el gasóleo, el gasoil** *ehl gas-oh-leh-oh, ehl gas-oh-eel*	**il diesel** *eel 'dee-sel*	**der Diesel** *derr diesel*
oil	**de l'huile** *de(r) lweel*	**el aceite** *ehl a-they-teh*	**l'olio** *'loh-lyoh*	**das Öl** *dass u(r)-l*
to hitch[1]	**faire du stop** *fair dew stop*	**hacer autostop** *a-thehr a-oo-toh-stohp*	**fare l'autostop** *'fah-reh 'low-toh-stop*	**trampen** *trampen*

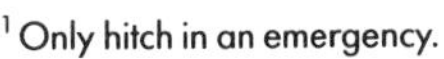

[1] Only hitch in an emergency.

Travel: breakdowns

	F
I've had an accident.	**J'ai eu un accident.** *Jeh ew un ak-see-do(n).*
Where's the nearest garage?	**Où est le garage le plus proche?** *Oo-eh le(r) ga-rahj le(r) plew prosh?*
I've run out of petrol.	**Je suis en panne d'essence.** *Je(r) swee o(n) pan desso(n)s.*
There's something wrong with...	**Il y a quelque chose qui ne va pas avec...** *Eel-ya kel-ke(r) shows kee ne(r) va pa a-vek...*
I have a puncture.	**J'ai crevé.** *Jeh kre(r)-veh.*
Can you fix it?	**Vous pouvez réparer ça?** *Voo poo-veh reh-pa-reh sa?*
How much will it cost?	**Ça coûtera combien?** *Sa koo-tra ko(m)bya(n)?*

Essential words

	F	S	I	G
jump leads	**les cables** *leh kahbl*	**los cables para la batería** *lohs ka-blehs pa-ra la ba-teh-ree-a*	**i cavetti** *ee ka-'vet-tee*	**die Starthilfekabel** *dee shtart-hillfe(r)-kahbel*
spark plugs	**les bougies d'allumage** *leh boo-jee da-lew-mahj*	**las bujías** *las boo-ghee-as*	**le candele** *leh kan-'deh-leh*	**die Zündkerzen** *dee tsewnt-kairtsen*
fan belt	**la courroie de ventilateur** *la koor-wa de(r) vo(n)-tee-la-tur*	**la correa del ventilador** *la koh-reh-a del behn-tee-la-dohr*	**la cinghia del ventilatore** *la 'cheen-gya del ven-tee-la-'toh-reh*	**der Keilriemen** *derr kile-reemen*
pump	**la pompe** *la po(m)p*	**el compresor de aire** *ehl kohm-preh-sohr deh a-ee-reh*	**la pompa** *la 'pom-pa*	**die Pumpe** *dee poompe(r)*
tyre	**le pneu** *le(r) pne(r)*	**el neumático** *ehl neh-oo-ma-tee-koh*	**il pneumatico** *eel pneh-oo-'ma-tee-koh*	**der Reifen** *derr ry-fen*
inner tube	**la chambre à air** *la sho(m)br a air*	**la cámara** *la ka-ma-ra*	**la camera d'aria** *la 'ka-meh-ra 'da-rya*	**der Schlauch** *derr shlowkh*

S	I	G
He tenido un accidente. *Eh teh-nee-doh oon ak-thee-dehn-teh.*	**Ho avuto un incidente.** *Oh a-'voo-to oon een-chee-'den-teh.*	**Ich habe einen Unfall gehabt.** *Ikh ha-be(r) eynen oon-fal ge(r)-hahbt.*
¿Dónde está el taller más cercano? *¿Dohn-deh ehs-ta ehl tal-yehr mas thehr-ka-noh?*	**Dov'è l'autofficina più vicina?** *'Doh-veh low-tof-fee-'chee-na pyoo vee-'chee-na?*	**Wo ist die nächste Werkstatt?** *Vo isst dee nekhste(r) vairk-shtat?*
Se me ha acabado la gasolina. *Seh meh a-ka-ba-doh la ga-soh-lee-na.*	**Ho finito la benzina.** *Oh fee-'nee-toh la ben-'tsee-na.*	**Mir ist das Benzin ausgegangen.** *Meer isst dass ben-zeen owss-ge(r)-gangen.*
Hay un fallo en... *A-ee oon fal-yoh ehn...*	**C'è qualcosa che non va nel...** *Cheh kwal-'koh-za keh non va nel...*	**... funktioniert nicht richtig.** *... foonk-tsee-owneert nikht rikh-tikh.*
Tengo un pinchazo. *Tehn-goh oon peen-tcha-thoh.*	**Ho forato.** *Oh foh-'ra-toh.*	**Ich habe einen Platten.** *Ikh ha-be(r) eynen platten.*
¿Puede repararlo usted? *¿Pweh-de reh-pa-rar-loh oos-teh?*	**Si può riparare?** *See 'pwoh ree-pa-'ra-reh?*	**Können Sie das reparieren?** *Ku(r)-nen zee dass re-par-reeren?*
¿Cuánto me costará? *¿Kwan-toh meh kohs-ta-ra?*	**Quanto viene a costare?** *'Kwan-toh vyeh-neh a kos-'ta-reh?*	**Was wird es kosten?** *Vass virt ess kosten?*

	F	S	I	G
radiator	le radiateur *le(r) radya-tur*	el radiador *ehl rad-ya-dohr*	il radiatore *eel ra-dya-'toh-reh*	der Kühler *derr kewler*
brakes	les freins *leh fra(n)*	los frenos *lohs freh-nohs*	i freni *ee 'freh-nee*	die Bremsen *dee bremzen*
lights	les phares *leh far*	las luces *las loo-thehs*	i fari *ee 'fa-ree*	die Scheinwerfer *dee shyn-vairfer*
battery	la batterie *la ba-tree*	la batería *la ba-teh-ree-a*	la batteria *la bat-teh-'ree-a*	die Batterie *dee batteree*
chain	la chaîne *la shen*	la cadena *la ka-deh-na*	la catena *la ka-'teh-na*	die Kette *dee kette(r)*
wheel	la roue *la roo*	la rueda *la rweh-da*	la ruota *la roo-'o-ta*	das Rad *dass raht*
gears	les vitesses *leh vee-tess*	las marchas *las mar-tchas*	le marce *leh 'mar-cheh*	die Gänge *dee genge(r)*
insurance certificate	le certificat d'assurance *le(r) sair-tee-fee-ka da-syew-ro(n)s*	la póliza de seguro *la poh-lee-tha deh seh-goo-roh*	il certificato di assicurazione *eel cher-tee-fee-'ka-toh dee as-see-koo-ra-'tsyoh-neh*	der Versicherungs-nachweis *derr fer-zikheroongs-nakh-vice*

Hotels and hostels

Making arrangements

	F	S
Do you have a room?	**Vous avez une chambre?** *Voo-za-veh ewn sha(m)br?*	**¿Tiene una habitación libre?** *¿Tyeh-neh oo-na a-bee-ta-thyon lee-breh?*
How much is it per night?	**Quel est le tarif pour une nuit?** *Kel-ay le(r) ta-reef poor ewn nwee?*	**¿Cuánto es por noche?** *¿Kwan-toh ehs pohr no-tcheh?*
Can I see the room?	**Je peux voir la chambre?** *Je(r) per vwa la sho(m)br?*	**¿Puedo ver la habitación?** *¿Pweh-doh behr la a-bee-ta thyon?*
I wish to stay from...to...	**Je voudrais rester du...au...** *Je(r) voo-dreh resteh dew...o...*	**Quisiera quedarme del...al...** *Kees-yeh-ra keh-dar-meh dehl...al...*
Is breakfast included?	**Le petit déjeuner est compris?** *Le(r) pe(r)-tee deh-je(r)-neh eh ko(m)-pree?*	**¿El desayuno está incluido?** *¿Ehl deh-sa-yoo-noh ehs-ta een-kloo-ee-doh?*

Hotel words

	F	S	I	G
double room	**une chambre pour deux personnes** *ewn sho(m)br poor de(r) pair-son*	**una habitación doble** *oo-na a-bee-ta-thyon doh-bleh*	**una camera doppia** *oona 'ka-meh-ra 'dop-pya*	**ein Doppelzimmer** *eyn doppel-tsim-mer*
single room	**une chambre pour une personne** *ewn sho(m)br poor ewn pair-son*	**una habitación individual** *oo-na a-bee-ta-thyon een-dee-bee-doo-al*	**una camera singola** *oona 'ka-meh-ra 'seen-goh-la*	**ein Einzelzimmer** *eyn eyn-tsell-tsimmer*
with bathroom	**avec salle de bains** *a-vek sal de(r) ba(n)*	**con baño** *kohn ba-nyoh*	**con bagno** *kon 'ban-nyoh*	**mit Bad** *mit baht*
lunch	**le déjeuner** *le(r) deh-je(r)-neh*	**la comida** *la koh-mee-da*	**il pranzo** *eel 'pran-tsoh*	**das Mittagessen** *dass mittak-essen*
dinner	**le dîner** *le(r) dee-neh*	**la cena** *la theh-na*	**la cena** *la 'cheh-na*	**das Abendessen** *dass ahbent-essen*
key	**la clé** *la kleh*	**la llave** *la lya-beh*	**la chiave** *la 'kya-veh*	**der Schlüssel** *derr shlewssel*
the bill	**l'addition** *la-dee-syon*	**la cuenta** *la kwehn-ta*	**il conto** *eel 'kon-toh*	**die Rechnung** *dee rekhnoong*

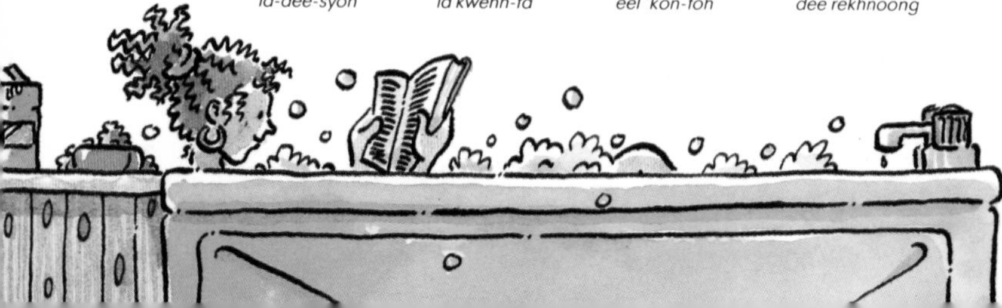

I	G
Avete una camera? *A-'veh-teh oona 'ka-meh-ra?*	**Haben Sie ein Zimmer?** *Ha-ben zee eyn tsimmer?*
Quant'è a notte? *Kwan-'teh a 'not-teh?*	**Was kostet es pro Nacht?** *Vass kostet ess pro nakht?*
Posso vedere la camera? *'Pos-so veh-'deh-reh la 'ka-meh-ra?*	**Kann ich das Zimmer sehen?** *Kan ikh dass tsimmer zay-en?*
Vorrei fermarmi dal...al... *Vor-'ray fehr-'mar-mee dal...al...*	**Ich möchte von... bis... bleiben.** *Ikh mu(r)khte(r) fon... biss... bly-ben.*
È inclusa la prima colazione? *Eh een-'cloo-sa la 'pree-ma koh-la-'tsyoh-neh?*	**Ist das mit Frühstück?** *Isst dass mit frew-shtook?*

Signs to look for

	F	S	I	G
hotel	hôtel *o-tel*	hotel *oh-tehl*	albergo, hotel *al-'behr-goh, oh-'tel*	Hotel *hotel*
youth hostel	auberge de jeunesse *o-bairj de(r) je(r)-ness*	albergue de juventud *al-behr-geh deh ghoo-behn-too*	ostello della gioventù *os-'tel-loh della joh- ven-'too*	Jugendherberge *yoo-ghent-hairbairge(r)*
guest house	chambre d'hôte *sho(m)-br dote*	pensión *pehn-syon*	pensione *pen-'syoh-neh*	Pension *pen-see-own*
rooms to let	chambres à louer *sho(m)br a loo-eh*	se alquilan habitaciones *seh al-kee-lan a-bee-ta-thyoh-nehs*	si affittano camere *see af-'feet-ta-noh 'ka-meh-reh*	Zimmer zu vermieten *tsimmer tsoo fer-meeten*
full board	pension *po(n)-syo(n)*	pensión completa *pehns-yohn kohm-pleh-ta*	pensione completa *pen-syoh-neh kom-'pleh-ta*	Vollpension *foll-pen-see-own*
half board	demi-pension *de(r)-mee po(n)-syo(n)*	media pensión *mehd-ya pehns-yohn*	mezza pensione *met-tsa pen-'syoh-neh*	Halbpension *halp-pen-see-own*
vacancies	chambres disponibles *sho(m)br dees-pon-eebl*	habitaciones libres *a bee-ta-thyoh-nehs lee-brehs*	camere libere *'ka-meh-reh 'lee-beh-reh*	Zimmer frei *tsimmer fry*
full	complet *ko(m)-pleh*	completo *kohm-pleh-toh*	al completo *al kom-'pleh-toh*	Ausgebucht *owss-ge-bookht*

Staying as a guest

Eating together

	F	S
What time is breakfast?[1]	A quelle heure prenez-vous le petit déjeuner? *A(h) kelu(r) pre(r)-neh voo le(r) pe(r)-tee deh-je(r)-neh?*	¿A qué hora es el desayuno? *¿A keh oh-ra ehs ehl deh-sa-yoo-noh?*
What's in this, please?	Qu'est-ce qu'il y a là dedans, s'il vous plait? *Kess-kee-lee-a(h) la de(r)da(n), seel-voo-pleh?*	¿De qué está hecho esto, por favor? *¿Deh keh ehs-ta eh-tchoh ehs-toh, pohr fa-bohr?*
I'm a vegetarian.	Je suis végétarien(-ne). *Je(r) swee veh-jeh-ta-rya(n)/ryen.*	Soy vegetariano(a). *Soh-ee beh-gheh-ta-rya-noh/na.*

Useful questions

	F
Where may I put my things?	Où est-ce que je peux mettre mes affaires? *Oo-wess-ke(r) je(r) pe(r) metr may-zaf-air?*
Could you wake me up at...?[1]	Vous pouvez me réveiller à...? *Voo poo-veh me(r) reh-veh-yeh a...?*
Can I have a key?	Je peux avoir une clé? *Je(r) pe(r) avwa ewn kleh?*
Can I use...?	Est-ce que je peux utiliser...? *Esske(r) je(r) pe(r) ew-tee-lee-zeh...?*
Can I borrow...?	Est-ce que je peux emprunter...? *Esske(r) je(r) pe(r) o(m)-pru(n)-teh...?*
Can I help?	Je peux vous aider? *Je(r) pe(r) voo-zed-eh?*

Helpful words

	F	S	I	G
bathroom	la salle de bain *la sal de(r) ba(n)*	el cuarto de baño *ehl kwar-toh deh ba-nyoh*	il bagno *eel 'ban-nyoh*	das Badezimmer *dass bahde(r)-tsimmer*
shower	la douche *la doosh*	la ducha *la doo-tcha*	la doccia *la 'doch-cha*	die Dusche *dee dooshe(r)*
towel	une serviette *ewn sair-vee-ette*	una toalla *oo-na toh-al-ya*	un asciugamano *oon a-shoo-ga-'ma-noh*	ein Handtuch *eyn hant-tookh*

[1] See pages 78-81 for times.

I	G
A che ora è la colazione? *A keh 'oh-ra eh la koh-la-'tsyoh-neh?*	**Wann gibt es Frühstück?** *Van gipt ess frew-shtewk?*
Mi può dire com'è fatto, per favore? *Mee 'pwoh 'dee-reh koh-'meh 'fat-toh, pehr fa-'voh-reh?*	**Was ist da drin, bitte?** *Vass isst dah drin, bitte(r)*
Sono vegetariano(a). *'Soh-noh veh-jeh-ta-'rya-noh/na.*	**Ich bin Vegetarier(-in).** *Ikh bin vegetarier/in.*

S	I	G
¿Dónde puedo dejar mis cosas? *¿Dohn-deh pweh-doh deh-ghar mees koh-sas?*	**Dove posso mettere la mia roba?** *'Doh-veh pos-soh 'met-teh-reh la 'mee-a 'roh-ba?*	**Wo soll ich mein Zeug hin tun?** *Vo zoll ikh mine tsoyg heen toon?*
¿Puede despertarme a las...? *¿Pweh-deh dehs-pehr-tar-meh a las...?*	**Potrebbe svegliarmi alle...?** *Poh-'treb-beh svel-'lyar-mee al-leh...?*	**Können Sie mich um ... wecken?** *Ku-(r)-nen zee mikh oom ... veken?*
¿Me puede dar una llave? *¿Meh pweh-deh dar oo-na lya-beh?*	**Potrei avere la chiave?** *Po-'tray a-'veh-reh la 'kya-veh?*	**Kann ich einen Schlüssel haben?** *Kan ikh eynen shlewsel ha-ben?*
¿Puedo usar...? *¿Pweh-doh oo-sar...?*	**Posso usare...?** *'Pos-soh oo-'za-reh...?*	**Kann ich ... benutzen?** *Kan ikh ... be-nootsen?*
¿Me deja...? *¿Meh deh-gha...?*	**Mi potrebbe dare ... in prestito?** *Mee poh-'treb-beh 'da-reh ... een 'pres-tee-toh?*	**Kann ich ... borgen?** *Kan ikh ... borgen?*
¿Puedo ayudar? *¿Pweh-doh a-yoo-dar?*	**Posso aiutare?** *'Pos-soh a-yoo-'ta-reh?*	**Kann ich helfen?** *Kan ikh helfen?*

	F	S	I	G
hairdryer	un sèche-cheveux *u(n) sesh-she(r)-ve(r)*	un secador *oon seh-ka-dohr*	un asciugacapelli *oon a-shoo-ga-ca-'pel-lee*	ein Fön *eyn fu(r)n*
iron	un fer à repasser *u(n) fair a re(r)-passeh*	una plancha *oo-na plan-tcha*	un ferro da stiro *oon 'fer-roh da 'stee-roh*	ein Bügeleisen *eyn bewgel-eyzen*
washing machine	la machine à laver *la masheen a laveh*	la lavadora *la la-ba-doh-ra*	la lavatrice *la la-va-'tree-cheh*	die Waschmaschine *dee vash-machine(r)*

Camping

	F	S
Can I camp here?	**Est-ce que je peux camper ici?** *Esske(r) je(r) pe(r) ko(m)-peh ee-see?*	**¿Puedo acampar aquí?** *¿Pweh-doh a-kam-par a-kee?*
What's the charge per night?	**Quel est le tarif par nuit?** *Kelleh le(r) tareef pa(r) nwee?*	**¿Cuánto cuesta por noche?** *¿Kwan-toh kwehs-ta pohr noh-tcheh?*
What facilities are there?	**Qu'est ce qu'il y a comme aménagements?** *Kess-kee-lya kom a-meh-na(h)-je(r)-mo(n)?*	**¿Qué instalaciones hay?** *¿Keh eens-ta-la-thyon-ehs a-ee?*
Is it OK to drink the tap water?	**On peut boire l'eau du robinet?** *O(n) pe(r) bwar lo dew ro-bee-neh?*	**¿Es potable el agua del grifo?** *¿Ehs poh-ta-bleh ehl a-gwa dehl gree-foh?*
The toilet is blocked.	**Les toilettes sont bouchées.** *Leh twa-let so(n) boo-sheh.*	**El lavabo está atascado.** *Ehl la-ba-boh ehs-ta atas-ka-doh.*
The shower is broken.	**La douche est cassée.** *La doosh eh kasseh.*	**La ducha está rota.** *La doo-tcha ehs-ta roh-ta.*

Essentials

	F	S	I	G
caravan	**une caravane** *ewn ka-ra-van*	**una caravana** *oo-na ka-ra-ba-na*	**una roulotte** *oona roo-'lot*	**ein Wohnwagen** *eyn vohn-vahgen*
tent	**une tente** *ewn to(n)t*	**una tienda** *oo-na tyehn-dah*	**una tenda** *oona 'ten-da*	**ein Zelt** *eyn tsellt*
sleeping bag	**un sac de couchage** *u(n) sak de(r) koo-shahj*	**un saco de dormir** *oon sa-koh deh dohr-meer*	**un sacco a pelo** *oon 'sak-koh a 'peh-loh*	**ein Schlafsack** *eyn shlahf-sak*
hot/cold water	**l'eau chaude/ froide** *lo sho-d/frwahd*	**el agua caliente/ fría** *ehl a-gwa kal-yehn-teh/free-a*	**l'acqua calda/ fredda** *'lak-kwa 'kal-da/ 'fred-da*	**warmes/kaltes Wasser** *var-mess/kal-tess vasser*
electric socket	**une prise de courant** *ewn preez de(r) koo-ra(n)*	**un enchufe** *oon ehn-tchoo-feh*	**una presa elettrica** *oona 'preh-za eh-'let-tree-ka*	**eine Steckdose** *eyne(r) shtek-doze(r)*
tent peg	**un piquet** *u(n) pee-keh*	**una estaquilla** *oo-na ehs-ta-keel-ya*	**un paletto** *oon pa-'let-toh*	**ein Hering** *eyn herring*
mallet	**un maillet** *u(n) my-yeh*	**un mazo** *oon ma-thoh*	**un maglio** *oon 'ma-lyoh*	**ein Holzhammer** *eyn holts-hammer*

I	G
È possibile campeggiare qui? *Eh pos-'see-bee-leh kam-pej-'ja-reh kwee?*	**Kann ich hier zelten?** *kan ikh heer tsell-ten?*
Quanto si paga per notte? *'Kwan-toh see 'pa-ga pehr 'not-teh?*	**Was kostet es pro Nacht?** *Vass kostet ess pro nahkht?*
Che servizi ci sono? *Keh sehr-'vee-tsee chee 'soh-noh?*	**Was gibt es als Einrichtungen?** *Vass gipt ess als eyn-rikhtoongen?*
È potabile l'acqua del rubinetto? *Eh poh-'ta-bee-leh 'lak-kwa del roo-bee-net-toh?*	**Kann man das Leitungswasser trinken?** *Can man dass lie-toonks-vasser trinken?*
Il gabinetto è bloccato. *Eel ga-bee-'net-toh eh blok-'ka-toh.*	**Die Toilette ist verstopft.** *Dee twa-lette(r) isst fer-shtopft.*
La doccia non funziona. *La 'doch-cha non foon-'tsyoh-na.*	**Die Dusche ist kaputt.** *Dee dooshe(r) isst kaput.*

	F	S	I	G
rubbish bags	les sacs poubelles *leh sak poo-bel*	las bolsas de basura *las bohl-sas deh ba-soo-ra*	i sacchetti della spazzatura *ee sak-'ket-tee del-la spat-tsa-'too-ra*	die Müllsäcke *dee mewl-zeke(r)*
torch	une lampe de poche *ewn lo(m)p de(r) posh*	una linterna *oo-na leen-tehr-na*	una torcia *oona 'tor-cha*	eine Taschenlampe *eyne(r) tashen-lampe(r)*
can opener	un ouvre-boîte *un-noo-vre(r) bwat*	un abrelatas *oon a-breh-la-tas*	un apriscatole *oon a-pree-'sca-toh-leh*	ein Dosenöffner *eyn dohzen-u(r)fner*
camping gas canister	une cartouche de camping-gaz *ewn kar-toosh de(r) komping-gaz*	una botella de camping gas *oo-na boh-tehl-ya deh kam-peen gas*	un fornellino da campeggio *oon for-nel-'lee-noh da kam-'pej-joh*	Campinggas Kanister *kamping-gas kan-nis-ter*
loo paper	du papier hygiénique *dew papyeh eejeh-neek*	el papel higiénico *ehl pa-pehl eegh-yeh-nee-koh*	la carta igienica *la 'kar-ta ee-'jeh-nee-ka*	das Klopapier *dass klo-papeer*
matches	des allumettes *dez alew-met*	las cerillas *las theh-reel-yas*	i fiammiferi *ee fyam-'mee-feh-ree*	die Streichhölzer *dee shtrykh-hu(r)ltser*

Banks and post offices

At the bank

	F
My bank is...	Ma banque est... *Ma bonk eh...*
I want to change some traveller's cheques.[1]	Je voudrais changer des traveller's chèques. *Je(r) voo-dreh sho(n)-jeh deh traveller's shek.*
I'm expecting some money.	J'attends de l'argent. *Ja-to(n) de(r) lar-ja(n).*

In the post office

	F
Can I have a stamp for this letter?	Je voudrais un timbre pour envoyer cette lettre. *Je(r) voo-dreh u(n) ta(m)br poor o(n)-vwa-yeh set letr.*
I want to send this parcel.	Je veux envoyer ce colis. *Je(r) ve(r) o(n)-vwa-yeh se(r) kolee.*

Bank words

	F	S	I	G
exchange rate	le cours du change *le(r) koor dew sho(n)j*	la tarifa de cambio *la ta-ree-fa deh kam-byoh*	il cambio *eel 'kam-byo*	der Wechselkurs *derr veksell-koors*
credit card	une carte de crédit *ewn kart de(r) kreh-dee*	una tarjeta de crédito *oo-na tar-gheh-ta deh kreh-dee-to*	una carta di credito *oo-na 'kar-ta dee 'kreh-dee-toh*	eine Kreditkarte *eyne(r) kredeet-karte(r)*
cashier's desk, till	la caisse *la kace*	la caja *la ka-gha*	la cassa *la 'kas-sa*	die Kasse *dee kasse(r)*
eurocheques	les eurochèques *leh ur-o-shek*	los eurocheques *los eh-oo-roh-tcheh-kehs*	gli eurocheques *ly 'ehoo-roh-cheks*	die Euroschecks *dee euro-sheks*
cash dispenser	le distributeur automatique *le(r) dee-stree-bew-tu(r) o-to-mat-eek*	el cajero automático *ehl ka-gheh-roh a-oo-toh-ma-tee-koh*	il bancomat *eel 'ban-koh-mat*	der Geldautomat *derr gelt-ow-toe-maht*

[1] Units of currency are – English: pound (£); French: franc (FF); Spanish: peseta (Pta); Italian: lira (L.it.); German: Deutsche Mark (DM).

S	I	G
Mi banco es... *Mee ban-koh ehs...*	**La mia banca è...** *La 'mee-a 'ban-ka eh...*	**Meine Bank ist...** *Mine(r) bank isst...*
Quiero cambiar cheques de viaje. *Kyeh-roh kam-byar tcheh-kehs deh bya-gheh.*	**Vorrei cambiare dei traveller's cheques.** *Vor-'ray kam-bya-reh day traveller's cheques.*	**Ich möchte Reiseschecks wechseln.** *Ikh mu(r)khte(r) ryze(r)-sheks vekseln.*
Estoy esperando un envío de dinero. *Ehs-toh-ee ehs-peh-ran-doh oon ehn-bee-oh deh dee-neh-roh.*	**Sto aspettando i soldi.** *Stoh as-pet-'tan-doh ee 'sol-dee.*	**Ich erwarte Geld.** *Ikh air-varte(r) gelt.*

S	I	G
¿Me da un sello para esta carta? *¿Meh da oon sehl-yoh pa-ra ehs-ta kar-ta?*	**Mi può dare un francobollo per questa lettera?** *Mee pwoh 'da-reh oon fran-co-'bol-lah pehr 'kwes-ta 'let-teh-ra?*	**Kann ich eine Briefmarke für diesen Brief haben?** *Kan ikh eyne(r) breef-marke(r) fewr dee-zen breef ha-ben?*
Quisiera enviar este paquete. *Kees-yeh-ra ehn-bee-ar ehs-teh pa-keh-teh.*	**Vorrei spedire questo pacco.** *Vor-'ray spe-'dee-reh 'kwes-toh 'pak-koh.*	**Ich möchte dieses Paket schicken.** *Ikh mu(r)khte(r) dee-zess pa-kate shi-ken.*

Postal words

	F	S	I	G
postbox	la boîte aux lettres *la bwat o letr*	el buzón *ehl boo-thohn*	la buca delle lettere *la 'boo-ka 'del-leh 'let-teh-reh*	der Brief-kasten *derr breef-kassten*
postcard	une carte postale *ewn kart posstal*	una postal *oo-na pohs-tal*	una cartolina *oona kar-toh-'lee-na*	eine Postkarte *eyne(r) posst-karte(r)*
envelope	une enveloppe *ewn o(n)-ve(r)-lop*	un sobre *oon soh--breh*	una busta *oona 'boos-ta*	ein Umschlag *eyn oom-shlahg*
by airmail	par avion *par a-vyo(n)*	por avión *pohr a-byon*	per via aerea *pehr 'vee-a a-'eh-reh-a*	per Luftpost *per looft-posst*
by registered mail	en recommandé *o(n) re(r)-kommo(n)-deh*	por correo certificado *pohr koh-reh-oh thehr-tee-fee-ka-doh*	per raccomandata *pehr rak-koh-man-'da-ta*	per Ein-schreiben *per eyn-shryben*
poste restante	poste restante *posst rest-o(n)t*	lista de correos *lees-ta deh koh-reh-ohs*	fermoposta *'fehr-moh-'pos-ta*	postlagernd *posst-lahgernd*

Making a phone call

	F	S
Where's the nearest phone booth?	**Où se trouve la cabine téléphonique la plus proche?** *Oo se(r) troov la ka-been teh-leh-foneek la plew prosh?*	**¿Dónde está la cabina de teléfono más cercana?** *¿Dohn-deh ehs-ta la ka-bee-na deh teh-leh-foh-noh mas thehr-ka-na?*
Can I use your phone?	**Je peux utiliser votre téléphone?** *Je(r) pe(r) ewtee-lee-zeh votr teh-leh-fon?*	**¿Puedo llamar por teléfono?** *¿Pweh-doh lya-mar pohr teh-leh-foh-noh?*
I can't get through.	**La communication ne passe pas.** *La kom-ew-nee-kassyo(n) ne(r) pass pa.*	**No puedo conectar.** *Noh pweh-doh koh-nehk-tar.*
We were cut off	**Nous avons été coupés.** *Noo-zavo(n) eh-teh koo-peh.*	**Se ha cortado.** *Seh a kohr-ta-doh.*
Do you speak English?	**Vous parlez anglais?** *Voo par-leh o(n)-gleh?*	**¿Habla inglés?** *¿A-bla een-glehs?*
Can I speak to . . . ?	**Est-ce que je peux parler à . . . ?** *Esske(r) je(r) pe(r) par-leh a . . . ?*	**¿Puedo hablar con . . . ?** *¿Pweh-doh a-blar kohn . . . ?*
My telephone number is . . . [1]	**Mon numéro est le . . .** *Mo(n) new-meh-ro eh le(r) . . .*	**Mi número es . . .** *Mee noo-meh-roh ehs . . .*

[1] See pages 78-81 for numbers.

Useful words

	F	S	I	G
directory	**l'annuaire** *la-new-air*	**el listín telefónico, la guía de teléfonos** *ehl lees-teen teh-leh-foh-nee-koh, la gee-a deh teh-leh-foh-nohs*	**l'elenco telefonico** *leh-'lehn-koh teh-leh-'foh-nee-koh*	**das Telefonbuch** *dass telefon-bookh*
directory enquiries	**les renseignements** *leh ro(n) senye(r)-mo(n)*	**información** *een-fohr-ma-thyon*	**le informazioni telefoniche** *leh een-for-ma-'tsyoh-nee teh-leh-'foh-nee-keh*	**die Auskunft** *dee ows-koonft*
operator	**l'opératrice** *loppeh-ra-treess*	**la operadora** *la oh-peh-ra-doh-ra*	**il centralino** *eel chen-tra-'lee-noh*	**die Vermittlung** *dee fer-mitloong*
reverse charge call	**un appel en PCV** *e(r)-na-pel o(n) peh-seh-veh*	**una llamada a cobro revertido** *oo-na lya-ma-da a koh-broh reh-behr-tee-doh*	**una chiamata a carico del destinatario** *oona kya-'ma-ta a ka-ree-koh del deh-stee-na-'ta-ryo*	**ein R-Gespräch** *eyn r-ge-shpraykh*

I	G
Dov'è la cabina telefonica più vicina? *'Doh-'veh la ka-'bee-na teh-leh-'foh-nee-ka pyoo vee-'chee-na?*	**Wo ist die nächste Telefonzelle?** *Vo isst dee nekhste(r) telefon-tselle(r)?*
Posso usare il telefono? *'Pos-soh oo-'za-reh eel teh-'leh-foh-noh?*	**Kann ich das Telefon benutzen?** *Can ikh dass telefon be-nootsen?*
Non riesco a prendere la linea. *Non 'reys-koh a 'pren-deh-reh la 'lee-neh-a.*	**Ich komme nicht durch.** *Ikh komme(r) nikht doorkh.*
È caduta la linea. *Eh ka-'doo-ta la 'lee-neh-a.*	**Wir wurden unterbrochen.** *Veer voor-den oonter-brokhen.*
Parla inglese? *'Par-la een-'gleh-zeh?*	**Sprechen Sie Englisch?** *Shprekhen zee english?*
Potrei parlare con . . . ? *Pot-'ray par-'la-reh con . . . ?*	**Kann ich . . . sprechen?** *Can ikh . . . shprekhen?*
Il mio numero di telefono è . . . *Eel 'mee-o 'noo-meh-roh dee teh-'leh-foh-noh eh . . .*	**Meine Nummer ist . . .** *Mine(r) noomer isst . . .*

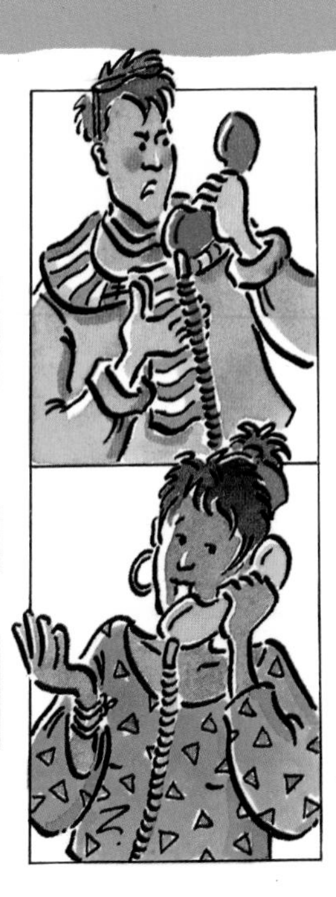

	F	S	I	G
code number	**l'indicatif** *la(n)-dee-kateef*	**el prefijo** *ehl preh-fee-ghoh*	**il prefisso telefonico** *eel preh-'fees-soh teh-leh-'foh-nee-koh*	**die Vorwahl** *dee For-vahl*
extension number	**le poste numéro** *le(r) posst new-meh-ro*	**el número de extensión** *ehl noo-meh-roh deh ex-tehn-syon*	**il numero interno** *eel 'noo-mehr-oh een-'tehr-noh*	**Apparat** *apparaht*
engaged	**occupé** *okew-peh*	**comunica** *koh-moo-nee-ka*	**occupato** *ok-koo-'pa-toh*	**besetzt** *be-zetst*
bad line	**une mauvaise ligne** *ewn mo-vez leen*	**una mala línea** *oo-na ma-la lee-neh-a*	**la linea disturbata** *la 'lee-neh-a dees-toor-'ba-ta*	**eine schlechte Verbindung** *eyne(r) shlekhte(r) fer-bin-doong*
wrong number	**le mauvais numéro** *le(r) mo-veh new-meh-ro*	**el número equivocado** *ehl noo-meh-roh eh-kee-boh-ka-doh*	**la numero sbagliato** *la 'noo-mehr-oh sbal-'lya-toh*	**falsch verbunden** *falsh fer-boonden*

Eating out

	F
Do you serve food?	**Vous servez à manger?** *Voo sair-veh a mo(n)jeh?*
Can we sit here?	**On peut s'asseoir ici?** *O(n) pe(r) sa-swa ee-see?*
Can I see the menu?	**Je peux voir la carte?** *Je(r) pe(r) vwah la kart?*

Helpful words

	F	S	I	G
restaurant	**un restaurant** *ewn res-tor-o(n)*	**un restaurante** *oon rehs-ta-oo-ran-teh*	**un ristorante** *oon ree-stoh-'ran-teh*	**ein Restaurant** *eyn restorant*
café	**un café, un bar** *u(n) kaffeh, u(n) bar*	**un café** *oon ka-feh*	**un bar** *oon bar*	**ein Café** *eyn kaffey*
starter	**l'entrée** *lo(n)-treh*	**el primer plato** *ehl pree-mehr pla-toh*	**l'antipasto** *lan-tee-'pas-toh*	**die Vorspeise** *dee for-shpyze*
main course	**le plat principal** *le(r) plah pra(n)-see-pal*	**el segundo plato** *ehl seh-goon-doh pla-toh*	**la portata principale** *la por-'ta-ta preen-chee-'pa-leh*	**das Hauptgericht** *dass howpt-ge(r)rikht*
dessert	**le dessert** *le(r) dess-air*	**el postre** *ehl pohs-treh*	**il dolce** *'dol-cheh*	**die Nachspeise, der Nachtisch** *dee nakh-shpyze(r), derr nakh-tish*

Drinks

	F	S	I	G
a bottle of...	**une bouteille de...** *ewn boo-tay de(r)...*	**una botella de...** *oo-na boh-tehl-ya deh...*	**una bottiglia di...** *oona bot-'teel-lya dee...*	**eine Flasche...** *eyne(r) flashe(r)...*
a glass of...	**un verre de...** *u(n) vair de(r)...*	**un vaso de...** *oon ba-soh deh...*	**un bicchiere di...** *oon beek-kyeh-reh dee...*	**ein Glas...** *eyn glass...*
...white/red wine	**vin blanc/rouge** *va(n) blo(n)/rooj*	**vino blanco/tinto** *vee-noh blan-koh/teen-toh*	**vino bianco/rosso** *'vee-no 'byan-koh/'ros-soh*	**Weißwein/Rotwein** *vice-vine/roat-vine*
mineral water	**une eau minérale** *ewn o mee-nair-ahl*	**un agua mineral** *oon a-gwa mee-neh-ral*	**un' acqua minerale** *oon 'ak-kwa mee-neh-ra-leh*	**ein Mineralwasser** *eyn mineral-vasser*
beer	**une bière** *ewn byair*	**una cerveza** *oo-na thehr-beh-tha*	**una birra** *oona 'beer-ra*	**ein Bier** *eyn beer*
draught beer	**une pression, un demi** *ewn pressyo(n), u(n) de(r)-mee*	**una caña** *oo-na ka-nya*	**una birra alla spina** *oona 'beer-ra al-la 'spee-na*	**ein Bier vom Faß** *eyn beer fom fass*

S	I	G
¿Sirven comidas? *¿Seer-behn koh-mee-das?*	**Servite da mangiare?** *Sehr-'vee-teh da man-'ja-reh?*	**Haben Sie etwas zu essen?** *Ha-ben zee etvass tsoo essen?*
¿Podemos sentarnos aquí? *¿Poh-deh-mohs sehn-tar-nohs a-kee?*	**Possiamo sederci qui?** *Pos-'sya-moh seh-'dehr-chee kwee?*	**Können wir hier sitzen?** *Ku(r)nen veer heer zitsen?*
¿Puedo ver el menú? *¿Pweh-doh behr ehl meh-noo?*	**Posso vedere il menù?** *'Pos-soh veh-'deh-reh eel me-'noo?*	**Die Karte, bitte.** *Dee karte(r), bitte(r).*

	F	S	I	G
tomato ketchup	**le ketchup** *le(r) ketchup*	**el ketchup** *ehl keh-tchop*	**il ketchup** *eel ketchup*	**das Tomatenketchup** *dass tomaten-ketchup*
dressing	**la vinaigrette** *la vee-neh-gret*	**la vinagreta** *la bee-na-greh-ta*	**il condimento** *eel kon-dee-'men-toh*	**die Salatsoße** *dee zalaht-zosse(r)*
mayonnaise	**la mayonnaise** *la mayo-naze*	**la mayonesa** *la ma-yoh-neh-sa*	**la maionese** *la ma-yoh-'neh-zeh*	**die Mayonnaise** *dee mayonayz*
mustard	**la moutarde** *la moo-tahd*	**la mostaza** *la mohs-ta-tha*	**la senape** *la 'seh-na-peh*	**der Senf** *derr zenf*
vinegar	**le vinaigre** *le(r) vee-neh-gr*	**el vinagre** *ehl bee-na-greh*	**l'aceto** *la 'cheh-toh*	**der Essig** *derr essikh*

	F	S	I	G
with ice	**avec des glaçons** *a-vek deh gla-so(n)*	**con hielo** *kohn yeh-loh*	**con ghiaccio** *kon 'gyach-choh*	**mit Eis** *mit eyss*
black coffee	**un café, un express** *u(n) kaffeh, un express*	**un café solo** *oon ka-feh soh-loh*	**un caffè** *oon kaf-'feh*	**ein schwarzer Kaffee** *eyn shvartse(r) kaffay*
white coffee	**un crème** *u(n) krem*	**un café con leche** *oon ka-feh kohn leh-tcheh*	**un caffè con latte** *oon kaf-'feh kon 'lat-teh*	**ein Milchkaffee** *eyn milkh-kaffay*
tea with milk	**un thé au lait** *u(n) teh o leh*	**un té con leche** *oon teh kohn leh-tcheh*	**un thè con latte** *oon teh kon 'lat-teh*	**ein Tee mit Milch** *eyn tay mit milkh*
lemon tea	**un thé-citron** *u(n) teh sit-ro(n)*	**un té con limón** *oon teh kohn lee-mohn*	**un thè al limone** *oon teh al lee-'moh-neh*	**ein Tee mit Zitrone** *eyn tay mit tsi-trone(r)*

Food

Fruit

	F	S	I	G
fruit	les fruits *leh frewee*	la fruta *la froo-ta*	la frutta *la 'froot-ta*	das Obst *dass obst*
I'd like...	Je voudrais... *Je(r) voo-dreh...*	Quisiera... *Kees-yeh-ra...*	Vorrei... *Vor-'ray...*	Ich möchte... *Ikh mu(r)khte(r).*
... apples	des pommes *deh pom*	unas manzanas *oo-nas man-tha-nas*	delle mele *'del-leh 'meh-leh*	Äpfel *ep-fel*
... oranges	des oranges *dez-or-o(n)j*	unas naranjas *oo-nas na-ran-ghas*	delle arance *'del-leh a-'ran-cheh*	Orangen *o-ran-jen*
... bananas	des bananes *deh ba-nan*	unos plátanos *oo-nohs pla-ta-nohs*	delle banane *'del-leh ba-'na-neh*	Bananen *bananen*

Vegetables and salad

	F	S	I	G
vegetables	les légumes *leh leh-gew-m*	las verduras *las behr-doo-ras*	la verdura *la vehr-'doo-ra*	Gemüse *ge(r)-mewze(r)*
salad	une salade *ewn sa-lahd*	una ensalada *oo-na ehn-sa-la-da*	un 'insalata *oona een-sa-'la-ta*	Salat *sa-laht*
I'd like...	Je voudrais... *Je(r) voo-dreh...*	Quisiera... *Kees-yeh-ra...*	Vorrei... *Vor-'ray...*	Ich möchte... *Ikh mu(r)khte(r).*
... carrots	des carottes *deh ka-rot*	unas zanahorias *oo-nas tha-na-oh-ryas*	delle carote *'del-leh ka 'roh-teh*	Karotten *karroten*
... cabbage	un chou *u(n) shoo*	una col *oo-na kohl*	un cavolo *oon 'ka-voh-loh*	einen Kohlkopf *eynen koal-kopf*
... peas	des petits pois *deh pe(r)-tee pwa*	unos guisantes *oo-nohs gee-san-tehs*	dei piselli *day pee-'sel-lee*	Erbsen *airbsen*
... potatoes	des pommes de terre *deh pom de(r) tair*	unas patatas *oo-nas pa-ta-tas*	delle patate *'del-leh pa-'ta-teh*	Kartoffeln *kartoffeln*
... courgettes	des courgettes *deh koor-jet*	unos calabacines *oo-nohs kah-la-ba-thee-nehs*	delle zucchine *'del-leh tsook-'kee-neh*	Zucchini *tsoo-keenee*

	F	S	I	G
... strawberries	des fraises *deh fraiz*	unas fresas *oo-nas freh-sas*	delle fragole *'del-leh-'fra-goh-leh*	Erdbeeren *aird-beeren*
... raspberries	des framboises *deh fro(m)-bwahz*	unas frambuesas *oo-nas fram-bweh-sas*	dei lamponi *day lam-'poh-nee*	Himbeeren *him-beeren*
... pears	des poires *deh pwa*	unas peras *oo-nas peh-ras*	delle pere *'del-leh 'peh-reh*	Birnen *beernen*
... peaches	des pêches *deh pesh*	unos melocotones *oo-nohs meh-loh-koh-toh-nehs*	delle pesche *'del-leh 'pes-keh*	Pfirsiche *pfeerzikhe(r)*
... nectarines	des brugnons *deh brew-nyo(n)*	unas nectarinas *oo-nas nek-ta-ree-nas*	delle peschenoci *'del-leh pes-keh-'noh-chee*	Nektarinen *nektarinnen*

	F	S	I	G
... green beans	des haricots verts *dez-aree-ko vair*	unas judías verdes *oo-nas ghoo-dee-as behr-dehs*	dei fagiolini *day fa-jo-'lee-nee*	grüne Bohnen *grewne(r) bo-nen*
... onions	des oignons *dez-onyo(n)*	unas cebollas *oo-nas theh-bohl-yas*	delle cipolle *'del-leh chee-'pol-leh*	Zwiebeln *tsweebeln*
... cauliflower	un chou-fleur *u(n) shoo-flu(r)*	una coliflor *oo-na koh-lee-flohr*	un cavolfiore *oon ka-vol-'fyoh-reh*	einen Blumenkohl *eynen bloomen-koal*
... peppers (red/ green)	des poivrons (rouges/verts) *deh pwa-vro(n) (rooj/vair)*	unos pimientos (rojos/verdes) *oo-nohs peem-yehn-tohs (roh-ghohs/behr-dehs)*	dei peperoni (rossi/verdi) *day peh-peh-'roh-nee ('ros-see/'vehr-dee)*	Paprikas (rot, grün) *pa-pree-kass (roat, grewn)*
... lettuce	une laitue *ewn leh-tew*	una lechuga *oo-na leh-tchoo-ga*	una lattuga *oona lat-'too-ga*	einen Kopfsalat *eynen kopf-zalaht*
... tomatoes	des tomates *deh tomaht*	unos tomates *oo-nohs toh-ma-tehs*	dei pomodori *day poh-moh-'doh-ree*	Tomaten *tomaten*
... cucumber	un concombre *u(n) ko(n)-ko(m)br*	un pepino *oon peh-pee-noh*	un cetriolo *oon cheh-'tryoh-loh*	eine Salatgurke *eyne(r) zalaht-goorke(r)*

Meat and fish

	F	S	I	G
meat	la viande *la vyo(n)d*	la carne *la kar-neh*	la carne *la 'kar-neh*	das Fleisch *dass flysh*
fish	le poisson *le(r) pwasso(n)*	el pescado *ehl pehs-ka-doh*	il pesce *eel 'peh-sheh*	der Fisch *derr fish*
I'd like…	Je voudrais… *Je(r) voo-dreh…*	Quisiera… *Kees-yeh-ra…*	Vorrei… *Vor-'ray…*	Ich möchte… *Ikh mu(r)khte(r)…*
…beef	du boeuf *dew bu(r)f*	carne de vaca *kar-neh deh ba-ka*	del manzo *del 'man-tzoh*	Rindfleisch *rind-flysh*
…chicken	du poulet *dew poo-leh*	un pollo *oon pohl-yoh*	del pollo *del 'pol-loh*	ein Hühnchen *eyn hewn-khen*
…continental sausage	du saucisson *dew soss-eess-o(n)*	chorizo *tchoh-ree-thoh*	del salame *del sa-'la-meh*	Wurst *vu(r)st*

Other food and drink

	F	S	I	G
I'd like…	Je voudrais… *Je(r) voo-dreh…*	Quisiera… *Kees-yeh-ra…*	Vorrei… *Vor-'ray…*	Ich möchte… *Ikh mu(r)khte(r)…*
…bread	du pain *dew pa(n)*	pan *pan*	del pane *del 'pa-neh*	Brot *broat*
…roll	un petit pain *u(n) pe(r)-tee pa(n)*	un panecillo *oon pa-neh-thee-lyoh*	un panino *oon pa-'nee-noh*	Brötchen *bru(r)t-chen*
…cheese	du fromage *dew from-ahj*	queso *keh-soh*	del formaggio *del for-'maj-joh*	Käse *kayze(r)*
…butter	du beurre *dew bu(r)*	mantequilla *man-teh-kee-lya*	del burro *del 'boor-roh*	Butter *booter*
…eggs	des oeufs *dezu(r)*	unos huevos *oo-nohs weh-bohs*	delle uova *'del-leh 'woh-va*	Eier *eyer*
…sugar	du sucre *dew sew-kr*	azúcar *a-thoo-kar*	dello zucchero *'del-loh 'tsook-keh-roh*	Zucker *tsooker*
…sandwich	un sandwich *u(n) so(n)d-veech*	un sandwich *oon sand-wee-tch*	un panino imbottito *oon pa-'nee-noh eem-bot-'tee-toh*	ein belegtes Brot *eyn be(r)-layg-te(r)s broat*
…chips	des frites *deh freet*	unas patatas fritas *oo-nas pa-ta-tas free-tas*	delle patate fritte *del-leh pat-'ta-teh 'freet-teh*	Fritten *fritten*
…pasta	des pâtes *deh paht*	pasta *pas-ta*	della pasta *'del-la 'pas-ta*	Nudeln *noodeln*
…rice	du riz *dew ree*	arroz *a-roth*	del riso *del 'ree-zoh*	Reis *rice*

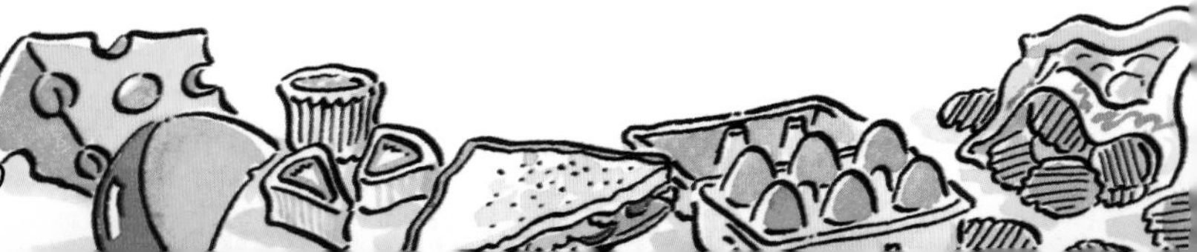

	F	S	I	G
...steak	**du steak** *dew stayk*	**un bistec** *oon bees-tehk*	**bistecca** *bees-'tek-ka*	**Steak** *shtayk*
...veal	**du veau** *dew vo*	**carne de ternera** *kar-neh deh tehr-neh-ra*	**del vitello** *del vee-'tel-loh*	**Kalbfleisch** *kalb-flysh*
...ham	**du jambon** *dew jom-bo(n)*	**jamón** *gha-mohn*	**del prosciutto** *del proh-'shoot-toh*	**Schinken** *shinken*
...seafood	**des fruits de mer** *deh frewee de(r) mair*	**mariscos** *ma-rees-kohs*	**dei frutti di mare** *day 'froot-tee dee 'ma-reh*	**Meeresfrüchte** *meer-es-frewkh-te(r)*
...prawns	**des crevettes** *deh kre(r)-vet*	**unas gambas** *oo-nas gam-bas*	**dei gamberetti** *day gam-beh- 'reh-tee*	**Krabben** *krabben*

	F	S	I	G
...crisps	**des chips** *deh sheep*	**unas patatas fritas** *oo-nas pa-ta-tas free-tas*	**delle patatine** *'del-leh pa-ta-'tee-neh*	**Chips** *ships*
...biscuits	**des biscuits** *deh bee-skwee*	**unas galletas** *oo-nas ga - lyeh-tas*	**dei biscotti** *day bees-'cot-tee*	**Kekse** *kekse(r)*
...ice cream	**une glace** *ewn glahs*	**un helado** *oon eh-la-doh*	**un gelato** *oon jeh-'la-toh*	**ein Eis** *eyn eyss*
...jam	**de la confiture** *de(r) la ko(n)-fee-tewr*	**mermelada** *mehr-meh-la-da*	**della marmellata** *'del-la mar-mel-'la-ta*	**Konfitüre** *kon-fitewre(r)*
...soup	**de la soupe, du potage** *de(r) la soop, dew pot-ahj*	**sopa** *soh-pa*	**della minestra, una zuppa** *'del-la mee-'nes-tra/oona 'tsoop-pa*	**Suppe** *zoope(r)*
...chocolate	**du chocolat** *dew shok-o-la*	**chocolate** *tchoh-koh-la-teh*	**del cioccolato** *del chok-koh-'la-toh*	**Schokolade** *shokolahde(r)*
...cake	**un gâteau** *u(n) gat-o*	**un pastel** *oon pas-tehl*	**una torta** *oona 'tohr-ta*	**Kuchen** *kookhen*
...fruit juice	**un jus de fruit** *u(n) jew de(r) frewee*	**un zumo de fruta** *oon thoo-moh deh froo-ta*	**un succo di frutta** *oon 'sook-ko dee 'froot-ta*	**einen Fruchtsaft** *eynen frookht-zaft*
...coke	**un coca** *u(n) ko-ka*	**una coca-cola** *oo-na koh-ka-koh-la*	**una coca cola** *oona 'koh-ka 'koh-la*	**eine Cola** *eyne(r) cola*
...milk	**du lait** *dew leh*	**leche** *leh-tcheh*	**del latte** *del 'lat-teh*	**Milch** *milkh*

Shopping

	F	S
I'm just looking.	**Je regarde seulement.** *Je(r) regard se(r)l-mo(n).*	**De momento, sólo quiero mirar.** *Deh moh-mehn-toh, soh-loh kyeh-roh mee-rar.*
I'll think about it.	**Je vais réfléchir.** *Je(r) veh reh-fleh-sheer.*	**Me lo pensaré.** *Meh loh pehn-sa-reh.*
Where can I get this repaired?	**Où est-ce que je peux faire réparer ça?** *Oo-esske(r) je(r) pe(r) fair reh-pa-reh sa?*	**¿Dónde pueden arreglarme esto?** *¿Dohn-deh pweh-dehn a-reh-glar-meh ehs-toh?*
Where can I get my film developed?	**Où est-ce que je peux faire développer ma pellicule?** *Oo-esske(r) je(r) pe(r) fair deh-vel-op-eh ma pellee-kewl?*	**¿Dónde puedo revelar un carrete?** *¿Dohn-deh pweh-doh reh-beh-lar oon ka-reh-teh?*
Where do I pay?	**Où dois-je payer?** *Oo dwa-j pay-eh?*	**¿Dónde tengo que pagar?** *¿Dohn-deh tehn-goh keh pa-gar?*

Essential shops

	F	S	I	G
Where is...	**Où est-ce qu'il y a...?** *Oo-esskeel-ya...?*	**¿Dónde está...?** *¿Dohn-deh ehs-ta...?*	**Dove si trova...?** *'Doh-veh see 'troh-va...?*	**Wo ist...?** *Vo isst...?*
...shopping centre	**le centre commercial** *le(r) so(n)tr kom-mair-syal*	**el centro comercial** *ehl thehn-troh koh-mehr-thyal*	**il centro** *eel 'chen-troh*	**das Einkaufszentrum** *dass eyn-kowfs-tsentrum*
...supermarket	**un supermarché, un libre-service** *u(n) syoo-pair-marsh-eh, u(n) lee-br sair-veess*	**un super, supermercado** *oon soo-pehr, soo-pehr-mehr-ka-doh*	**un supermercato** *oon soo-pehr-mehr-ka-toh*	**ein Supermarkt** *eyn supermarkt*
...delicatessen	**une charcuterie, un traiteur** *ewn shah-kew-tree, u(n) tray-tu(r)*	**una charcutería** *oo-na tchar-koo-teh-ree-a*	**un negozio di specialità gastronomiche** *oon neh-'goh-tsyoh dee speh-cha-lee-'ta ga-stroh-'noh-mee-keh*	**ein Delikateßge-schäft** *eyn delikatess-ge(r)sheft*
...butcher	**une boucherie** *ewn boo-shree*	**una carnicería** *oo-na kar-nee-theh-ree-a*	**un macellaio** *oon ma-chell-'eye-o*	**eine Metzgerei, eine Schlachterei** *eyne(r) mets-ge(r)-ry, eyne(r) shlahkhte(r)-ry*
...greengrocer	**un marchand de fruits et légumes** *u(n) marsho(n) de(r) frewee eh leh-gewm*	**una verdulería** *oo-na behr-doo-leh-ree-a*	**un fruttivendolo** *oon froot-tee-'ven-doh-loh*	**ein Obst und Gemüsehändler** *eyn obst-oont ge(r)mewze-hendler*
...baker	**une boulangerie** *ewn boolo(n)-jree*	**una panadería** *oo-na pa-na-deh-ree-a*	**un panificio** *oon pa-nee-'fee-choh*	**eine Bäckerei** *eyne(r) becke(r)-ry*

I	G
Sto solo dando un'occhiata. *Stoh 'soh-loh 'dan-doh oon ok-'kya-ta.*	**Ich sehe mich nur um.** *Ikh zaye(r) mikh noor oom.*
Ci voglio pensare un po'sù. *Chee 'vol-lyoh pen-'sa-reh oon 'poh'soo.*	**Ich überleg's mir.** *Ikh ewber-laygs meer.*
Dove posso far riparare questo/a? *'Doh-veh 'pos-soh far ree-pa-'ra-reh 'kwestoh/ta?*	**Wo kann ich das reparieren lassen?** *Vo kan ikh dass repareeren lassen?*
Dove posso portare a far sviluppare il rullino? *'Doh-veh 'pos-soh por-'ta-reh a far svee-loop-'pa-reh eel rool-lee-noh?*	**Wo kann ich meinen Film entwickeln lassen?** *Vo kan ikh minen film ent-vikeln lassen?*
Dove si paga? *'Doh-veh see 'pa-ga?*	**Wo bezahlt man?** *Vo be(r)tsahlt man?*

	F	S	I	G
... chemist	**une pharmacie** *ewn farma-see*	**una farmacia** *oo-na far-ma-thya*	**una farmacia** *oona far-ma-'chee-a*	**eine Apotheke**[1] *eyne(r) a-po-tayke(r)*
... newsagent	**un marchand de journaux** *u(n) marsho(n) de(r) joor-no*	**un quiosco** *oon kyohs-koh*	**un giornalaio** *oon johr-na-'la-yoh*	**ein Zeitungshändler** *eyn tsytoongs-hendler*
... market	**un marché** *u(n) marsh-eh*	**un mercado** *oon mehr-ka-doh*	**un mercato** *oon mehr-'ka-toh*	**ein Markt** *eyn markt*
... gift shop	**une boutique de cadeaux** *ewn boo-teek de(r) kad-o*	**una tienda de objetos de regalo** *oo-na tyehn-da deh oh-gheh-tohs deh reh-ga-loh*	**un negozio di articoli da regalo** *oon neh-'goh-tsyoh dee ar-'tee-koh-lee da reh-'ga-loh*	**ein Geschenkartikel-geschäft** *eyn ge(r)shenk-artikel-ge(r)sheft*
... travel agent	**une agence de tourisme** *ewn a-jo(n)ss de(r) too-reezm*	**una agencia de viajes** *oo-na a-ghehn-thya deh bya-ghehs*	**un'agenzia turistica** *oon a-jen-'tsee-a too-'ree-stee-ka*	**ein Reisebüro** *eyn ryze(r)bewro*
... optician	**un opticien** *u(n) op-tee-sya(n)*	**una óptica** *oo-na ohp-tee-ka*	**un ottico** *oon 'ot-tee-koh*	**ein Optiker** *eyn optiker*

[1] A non-dispensing chemist in Germany is eine Drogerie *(eyne(r) drogeree).*

Shopping lists

	F	S	I	G
I'd like...	Je voudrais... *Je(r) voo-dreh...*	Quisiera... *Kees-yeh-ra...*	Vorrei... *Vor-'ray...*	Ich möchte... *Ikh mu(r)khte(r)...*
...newspaper	un journal *u(n) joor-nal*	un periódico *oon pehr-yoh-dee-koh*	un giornale *oon johr-'na-leh*	eine Zeitung *eyne(r) tsy-toong*
...English newspapers	des journaux anglais *deh joor-no o(n)-gleh*	unos periódicos ingleses *oo-nohs pehr-yoh-dee-kohs een-gleh-sehs*	dei giornali inglesi *day johr-'na-lee eeng-'gleh-zee*	englische Zeitungen *englishe(r) tsy-toongen*
...writing paper	du papier à lettres *dew pa-pyeh a letr*	papel de escribir *pa-pehl deh ehs-kree-beer*	della carta da lettere *'del-la 'kar-ta da 'let-teh-ra*	Schreibpapier *shryb-pa-peer*
...pen	un stylo *u(n) stee-lo*	un bolígrafo *oon boh-lee-gra-foh*	una penna *oona 'pen-na*	einen Stift *eynen shtift*
...cotton/needle	du fil/une aiguille *dew feel/ewn ay-gwee-ye(r)*	hilo/una aguja *ee-loh/oo-na a-goo-gha*	del cotone/un'ago *del koh-'toh-neh/oon'a-goh*	Faden/eine Nadel *fah-den/eyne(r) nahdel*
...battery	une pile *ewn peel*	una pila *oo-na pee-la*	una pila *oona 'pee-la*	eine Batterie *eyne(r) batteree*
...stamps	des timbres *deh ta(m)br*	unos sellos *oo-nohs sehl-yohs*	dei francobolli *day fran-koh-'bol-lee*	Briefmarken *breef-marken*
...film	une pellicule *ewn pellee-kewl*	un carrete *oon ka-reh-teh*	un rullino *oon rool-'lee-noh*	ein film *eyn film*

Personal essentials

	F	S	I	G
...aspirins	des aspirines *dez aspee-reen*	unas aspirinas *oo-nas as-pee-ree-nas*	aspirine *as-pee-'ree-neh*	Aspirin *aspee-reen*
...plasters	du sparadrap *dew spa-ra-dra*	unas tiritas *oo-nas tee-ree-tas*	dei cerotti *day cheh-'rot-tee*	Pflaster *pflaster*
...sunblock	un écran total *un ek-ro(n) to-tal*	una crema con protectión total *oo-na kreh-ma kohn proh-tehk-thyon toh-tal*	una crema con schermo solare *oona 'kreh-ma kon 'skehr-moh so-'la-reh*	ein Sonnenschutz-mittel *eyn zonnen-shoots-mittel*
...sun-tan lotion	une crème solaire *ewn krem solair*	una crema bronceadora *oo-na kreh-ma brohn-theh-a-doh-ra*	della crema abbronzante *'del-la 'kreh-ma ab-bron-'tzan-teh*	Sonnencreme *zonnen-kreme(r)*
...tissues	des mouchoirs en papier *deh moo-shwa o(n) pa-pyeh*	unos pañuelos de papel *oo-nohs pa-nweh-lohs deh pa-pehl*	dei fazzolettini di carta *day fat-tso-let-'tee-nee dee 'kar-ta*	Papiertaschen-tücher *pa-peer-tashen-tewkher*

	F	S	I	G
... insect repellent	une lotion antimoustique *ewn lo-syo(n) o(n)tee-moo-steek*	una loción contra insectos *oo-na loh-thyon kohn-tra een-sehk-tohs*	una lozione anti-insetti *oona loh-'tsyoh-neh an-tee-een-'set-tee*	ein Insektenschutz-mittel *eyn insecten-shootz-mittel*
... condoms	des préservatifs *deh pray-zair-va-teef*	unos condones *oo-nohs kohn-doh-nehs*	dei preservativi, profilattici *day preh-sehr-va-'tee-vee, proh-fee-'lat-tee-chee*	Präservative, Kondome *pray-zairvateeve(r), kondome(r)*
... sanitary towels	des serviettes hygiéniques *deh sair-vee-et ee-jeh-neek*	unas compresas *oo-nas kohm-preh-sas*	degli assorbenti *'del-lee as-sor-'ben-tee*	Binden *bin-den*
... tampons	des tampons *deh to(m)-po(n)*	unos tampones *oo-nohs tam-poh-nehs*	dei tamponi *day tam-'poh-nee*	Tampons *tampons*
... toothpaste	du dentifrice *dew do(n)-tee-freess*	pasta de dientes *pas-ta deh dyehn-tehs*	del dentifricio *del den-tee-'free-choh*	Zahnpasta *tsahn-pasta*
... soap	un savon *u(n) sa-vo(n)*	jabón *gha-bohn*	del sapone *del sa-'poh-neh*	Seife *zyfe(r)*
... toilet paper	du papier hygiénique *dew pa-pyeh ee-jeh-neek*	papel higiénico *pa-pehl eegh-yeh-nee-koh*	della carta igienica *del-la 'kar-ta ee-'jeh-nee-ka*	Klopapier *klo-pa-peer*
... washing powder	de la lessive *de(r) la less-eev*	detergente *deh-tehr-ghehn-teh*	del detersivo *del deh-tehr-'see-voh*	Waschpulver *vash-poolver*
... shampoo	du shampooing *dew shampooing*	champú *tcham-poo*	dello shampoo *del-loh 'sham-poh*	Shampoo *shampoo*
... razor	un rasoir *u(n) ra-zwa(r)*	una maquinilla de afeitar *oo-na ma-kee-nee-lya deh a-feh-ee-tar*	un rasoio *oon ra-'zoh-yoh*	einen Rasierapparat *eynen ra-zeer-apparaht*
... shaving foam	de la crème à raser *de(r) la krem a ra-zeh*	espuma de afeitar *ehs-poo-ma deh a-feh-ee-tar*	della schiuma da barba *'del-la 'skyoo-ma da 'bar-ba*	Rasierschaum *ra-zeer-showm*
... deodorant	un déodorant *u(n) deh-odo-ro(n)*	un desodorante *oon deh-soh-doh-ran-teh*	un deodorante *oon deh-oh-doh-'ran-teh*	einen Deodorant *eynen dayodorant*
... contact lens solution	de la solution de nettoyage (pour lentilles) *de(r) la solew-syo(n) de(r) netwa-yahj (poor lo(n)-tee-ye(r))*	solución para las lentes de contacto *soh-loo-thyon pa-ra las lehn-tehs deh kohn-tak-toh*	una soluzione per le lenti a contatto *oona soh-loo-'tsyoh-neh pehr leh 'len-tee a kon-'tat-toh*	Kontaktlinsen flüssigkeit *kontakt-linzen flewsikh-kite*

Clothes

Buying clothes

	F
Can I try this on?	**Je peux essayer ça?** *Je(r) pe(r) essay-eh sa?*
Do you have it in another colour?[1]	**Vous avez ça d'une autre couleur?** *Voo-zaveh sa dew-no-tr koo-lu(r)?*
Can goods be returned?	**Est-ce que vous reprenez la marchandise?** *Esske(r) voo re(r)-pre(r)neh la marsho(n)-deez?*
changing rooms	**les cabines d'essayage** *leh ka-been dess-eh-ahj*

Things to wear

	F	S	I	G
clothes	**les vêtements** *leh vet-mo(n)*	**la ropa** *la roh-pa*	**abbigliamento** *ab-beel-lya-'men-toh*	**Kleider** *klyder*
shirt	**une chemise** *ewn she(r)-meez*	**una camisa** *oo-na ka-mee-sa*	**una camicia** *oona ka-'mee-cha*	**ein Hemd** *eyn hemd*
T-shirt	**un tee-shirt** *u(n) tee-shirt*	**una camiseta** *oo-na ka-mee-seh-ta*	**una maglietta** *oona mal-'lyet-ta*	**ein T-shirt** *eyn T-shirt*
sweatshirt	**un sweat-shirt** *u(n) swet-shirt*	**un suéter** *oon sweh-tehr*	**una felpa** *oona 'fel-pa*	**ein Sweatshirt** *eyn sweatshirt*
sweater	**un pull** *u(n) pool*	**un jersey** *oon ghehr-seh-ee*	**un maglione** *oon mal-'lyoh-neh*	**ein Pulli** *eyn pooli*
dress	**une robe** *ewn rob*	**un vestido** *oon behs-tee-doh*	**un vestito** *oon ves-'tee-toh*	**ein Kleid** *eyn klyd*
skirt	**une jupe** *ewn jewp*	**una falda** *oo-na fal-da*	**una gonna** *oona 'gon-na*	**ein Rock** *eyn rock*
leggings	**des jambières** *deh jo(m)-byair*	**unos leotardos** *oo-nohs leh-oh-tar-dohs*	**dei pantacollant** *day pan-ta-kol-'lant*	**Leggings** *leggings*
trousers	**un pantalon** *u(n) po(n)-ta-lo(n)*	**unos pantalones** *oo-nohs pan-ta-loh-nehs*	**i pantaloni** *ee pan-ta-'loh-nee*	**Hosen** *hozen*
jeans	**un jean** *u(n) jeen*	**unos vaqueros, unos tejanos** *oo-nohs ba-keh-rohs, oo-nohs teh-gha-nohs*	**i jeans** *ee jeans*	**Jeans** *jeans*
trainers	**des baskets** *deh bas-keh*	**unas zapatillas de deporte** *oo-nas tha-pa-tee-yas deh deh-pohr-teh*	**le scarpe da ginnastica** *leh 'skar-peh da jeen-'na-stee-ka*	**Turnschuhe** *toorn-shoe(r)*

S	I	G
¿Puedo probarme esto? *¿Pweh-doh proh-bar-meh ehs-toh?*	**Me lo/la posso misurare?** *Meh loh/la 'pos-soh mee-zoo-'ra-reh?*	**Kann ich das anprobieren?** *Kan ikh dass an-pro-beeren?*
¿Lo tienen en otro color? *¿Loh tyeh-nehn ehn oh-troh koh-lohr?*	**Ce l'avete anche in altri colori?** *Cheh la-'veh-teh 'an-keh een 'al-tree koh-'loh-ree?*	**Haben Sie das in einer anderen Farbe?** *Ha-ben zee dass in eyner anderen far-be(r)?*
¿Admiten devoluciones? *¿Ad-mee-tehn deh-boh-loo-thyoh-nehs?*	**Posso portarlo indietro se non va bene?** *'Pos-soh por-'tar-loh een-'dyeh-troh seh non va'beh-neh?*	**Kann man Sachen umtauschen?** *Kan man zakhen oom-towshen?*
los probadores *lohs proh-ba-doh-rehs*	**gli spogliatoi** *llee spo-lya-'toh-ee*	**Umkleidekabinen** *oom-klyde(r)-kabinen*

	F	S	I	G
shoes	**des chaussures** *deh sho-syoor*	**unos zapatos** *oo-nohs tha-pa-tohs*	**le scarpe** *leh 'skar-peh*	**Schuhe** *shoe(r)*
jacket	**une veste** *ewn vest*	**una chaqueta** *oo-na tcha-keh-ta*	**una giacca** *oona 'jak-ka*	**eine Jacke** *eyne(r) yacke(r)*
boxer shorts	**un caleçon** *u(n) kal-so(n)*	**unos calzoncillos** *oo-nohs kal-thohn-thee-yohs*	**i boxer** *ee 'bok-sehr*	**Boxershorts** *boxershorts*
bra	**un soutien-gorge** *u(n) soo-tya(n)-gorj*	**un sujetador** *oon soo-gheh-ta-dohr*	**un reggiseno** *oon rehj-jee-'seh-noh*	**ein BH** *eyn bay-ha*
briefs	**un slip** *u(n) sleep*	**unas bragas** *oo-nas bra-gas*	**le mutande** *leh moo-'tan-deh*	**eine Unterhose** *eyn oonter-hoze(r)*
tights	**un collant** *u(n) kollo(n)*	**unas medias** *oo-nas meh-dyas*	**le collant** *leh kol-'lant*	**eine Strumpfhose** *eyne(r) shtroompf-hose(r)*
socks	**des chaussettes** *deh sho-set*	**unos calcetines** *oo-nohs kal-theh-tee-nehs*	**i calzini** *ee kal-'tsee-nee*	**Socken** *zocken*
swimsuit	**un maillot** *u(n) my-yo*	**un bañador** *oon ba-nya-dohr*	**un costume da bagno** *oon kos-too-meh da 'ban-nyo*	**ein Badeanzug** *eyn bahde(r)-an-tsook*

Sizes

small	**petit (-e)** *pe(r)-tee/t*	**pequeño(a)** *peh-keh-nyoh/nya*	**piccolo(a)** *'peek-koh-loh/la*	**klein/e** *kline/e(r)*
medium	**moyen(-ne)** *mwa-ya(n)/yen*	**mediano(a)** *meh-dya-noh/na*	**medio(a)** *'meh-dyoh*	**medium** *may-dium*
large	**grand(-e)** *gro(n)/d*	**grande** *gran-deh*	**grande** *'gran-deh*	**groß/e** *gross/e(r)*

[1] See Index for colours.

Looking for work

Making enquiries

	F
I'm looking for a job.	**Je cherche du travail.** *Je(r) shairsh dew trav-eye.*
Do you have any vacancies?	**Est-ce que vous embauchez?** *Esske(r) voo-zo(m)-bo-sheh?*
What are the hours?	**Quels sont les horaires?** *Kell so(n) lez o-rair?*
What do you pay?	**Quel est le salaire?** *Kelleh le(r) sa-lair?*
What do I have to do?	**Qu'est-ce que je dois faire?** *Kesske(r) je(r) dwa fair?*
When/how do we get paid?	**Quand/comment est-on payé?** *Ko(n)/komo(n) etto(n) payeh?*

Job opportunities

	F	S	I	G
bar work	**du travail dans un bar** *dew trav-eye do(n)z-u(n) bar*	**trabajo de bar** *tra-ba-ghoh deh bar*	**lavoro da barista** *la-'voh-roh da ba-'ree-sta*	**Arbeit hinter der Theke** *arbite hinter derr tayke(r)*
kitchen work	**la plonge** *la plo(n)j*	**trabajo de cocina** *tra-ba-ghoh deh koh-thee-na*	**aiuto in cucina** *a-'yoo-toh een koo-'chee-na*	**Küchenarbeit** *kewkhen-arbite*
shop assistant	**un vendeur/une vendeuse** *u(n) vo(n)-du(r)/ ewn vo(n)-du(r)z*	**un dependiente/ una dependienta** *oon deh-pehn-dyehn-teh/oo-na deh-pehn-dyehn-ta*	**un commesso/ una commessa** *oon kom-'mes-soh/ oona kom-'mes-sa*	**ein Verkäufer/ eine Verkäuferin** *eyn fer-koyfer/ eyne(r) fer-koyfer-in*
waiter/waitress	**un serveur/une serveuse** *u(n) sair-vu(r)/ewn sair-vu(r)z*	**un camarero/una camarera** *oon ka-ma-reh-roh/oo-na kah-mah-reh-rah*	**un cameriere/una cameriera** *oon ka-meh-'ryeh-reh/oona ka-meh-'ryeh-ra*	**ein Kellner/eine Kellnerin** *eyn kellner/eyne(r) kellner-in*
chamber maid	**une femme de chambre** *ewn fam de(r) sho(m)br*	**una camarera, doncella** *oo-na ka-ma-reh-ra, dohn-theh-la*	**una domestica** *oona do-'mes-tee-ka*	**ein Zimmermädchen** *eyn tsimmer-medchen*
babysitter	**un/une babysitter** *u(n)/ewn babysitter*	**un cuidador/una cuidadora de niños** *oon kwee-da-dohr/ oo-na kwee-da-dohr-a deh nee-nyohs*	**un/una babysitter** *oon/oona beh-bee-'seet-tehr*	**ein Babysitter** *eyn babyzitter*

S	I	G
Busco trabajo. *Boos-koh tra-ba-ghoh.*	**Sto cercando lavoro.** *Stoh cher-'kan-doh la-'voh-roh.*	**Ich suche einen Job.** *Ikh zookhe(r) eynen job.*
¿Tiene puestos de trabajo? *¿Tyeh-neh pwehs-tohs deh tra-ba-ghoh?*	**Avete dei posti di lavoro liberi?** *A-'veh-teh 'day 'pos-tee dee la-'voh-roh 'lee-beh-ree?*	**Stellen Sie jemanden ein?** *Shtellen zee yay-manden eyn?*
¿Cuántas horas hay que trabajar? *¿Kwan-tas oh-ras a-ee keh tra-ba-ghar?*	**Quali sono gli orari?** *'Kwa-lee 'soh-noh llyee oh-'ra-ree?*	**Wie sind die Arbeitszeiten?** *Vee sint dee arbites-tsiten?*
¿Cuál es el sueldo? *¿Kwal ehs ehl swehl-doh?*	**Che paga offrite?** *Keh 'pa-ga of-'free-teh?*	**Wieviel bezahlen Sie?** *Vee-feel be(r)-tsahlen zee?*
¿Qué tengo que hacer? *¿Keh tehn-goh keh a-thehr?*	**Cosa dovrei fare?** *'Koh-za do-'vray 'fa-reh?*	**Was muß ich tun?** *Vass moos ikh toon?*
¿Cuándo/cómo nos pagan? *¿Kwan-doh/koh-moh nohs pa-gan?*	**Quando/come ci pagate?** *'Kwan-doh/'koh-meh chee pa-'ga-teh?*	**Wann/wie werden wir bezahlt?** *Van/vee vair-den veer be(r)-tsahlt?*

	F	S	I	G
nanny	**une nourrice** *ewn noo-reess*	**una niñera** *oo-na nee-nyeh-ra*	**un/una governante** *oon/oona goh-vehr-'nan-teh*	**ein Kindermädchen** *eyn kinder-medchen*
fruit picker	**un cueilleur de fruits** *u(n) ke(r)-yer de(r) frewee*	**un recolector/una recolectora de fruta** *oon reh-koh-lehk-tohr/oo-na reh-koh-lehk-toh-ra deh froo-ta*	**un raccoglitore/una raccoglitrice di frutta** *oon rak-kol-lyee-'toh-reh/oona rak-kol-lyee-'tree-cheh dee 'froot-ta*	**ein Obstpflücker/eine Obstpflückerin** *eyn obst-pflewker/eyne(r) obst-pflewker-in*

Helpful words

	F	S	I	G
full-time	**à plein temps** *a pla(n) to(n)*	**jornada completa** *ghohr-na-da kohm-pleh-ta*	**a tempo pieno** *a 'tem-poh 'pyeh-noh*	**Vollzeit** *foll-tsite*
part-time	**à mi-temps** *a mee to(n)*	**jornada reducida** *ghohr-na-da reh-doo-thee-da*	**mezza giornata** *'met-tsa johr-'na-ta*	**Teilzeit** *tile-tsite*
lunchbreak	**la pause-déjeuner** *la po-z deh-ju(r)-neh*	**la hora de la comida** *la oh-ra deh la koh-mee-da*	**l'intervallo per il pranzo** *leen-tehr-'val-loh pehr eel 'pran-tsoh*	**die Mittagspause** *dee mittahks-powze(r)*
day off	**un jour de congé** *u(n) joor de(r) ko(n)-jeh*	**un día libre** *oon dee-a lee-breh*	**una giornata libera** *oona johr-'na-ta 'lee-behr-ra*	**ein freier Tag** *eyn frye(r) tahk*

Studying

	F
What are you studying?	**Qu'est ce que tu fais comme études?** *Kesske(r) tew feh kom-eh-tewd?*
Where can I buy second-hand books?	**Où est-ce que je peux acheter des livres d'occasion?** *Oo-esske(r) je(r) pe(r) ash-teh deh leevr dok-azyo(n)?*
How do I join the library?	**Comment puis-je m'inscrire à la bibliothèque?** *Komo(n) pweej ma(n)-skreer a la bee-blyo-tek?*

Subjects

	F	S	I	G
maths	**les maths** *leh mat*	**matemáticas, mates** *ma-teh-ma-tee-kas, ma-tehs*	**matematica** *ma-teh-'ma-tee-ka*	**Mathematik** *ma-te(r)-ma-teek*
German	**l'allemand** *lal-mo(n)*	**alemán** *a-leh-man*	**tedesco** *teh-'des-koh*	**Deutsch** *doych*
French	**le français** *le(r) fro(n)-seh*	**francés** *fran-thehs*	**francese** *fran-'cheh-zeh*	**Französisch** *franzu(r)zish*
Italian	**l'italien** *lee-tal-ya(n)*	**italiano** *ee-ta-lya-noh*	**italiano** *ee-ta-'lya-noh*	**Italienisch** *italee-aynish*
Spanish	**l'espagnol** *less-panyol*	**español** *ehs-pa-nyohl*	**spagnolo** *span-'nyoh-loh*	**Spanisch** *shpahnish*
art	**le dessin** *le(r) deh-ssa(n)*	**arte** *ar-teh*	**educazione artistica** *eh-doo-ka-'tsyo-neh ar-'tee-stee-ka*	**Kunst** *koonst*
history	**l'histoire** *lee-stwa(r)*	**historia** *ees-tohr-ya*	**storia** *'stoh-rya*	**Geschichte** *ge(r)shikhte(r)*
geography	**la géographie** *la jeh-ografee*	**geografía** *gheh-oh-gra-fee-a*	**geografia** *jeh-o-gra-'fee-a*	**Geographie** *gay-ographee*
chemistry	**la chimie** *la shimee*	**química** *kee-mee-ka*	**chimica** *'kee-mee-ka*	**Chemie** *khemee*
physics	**la physique** *la fiz-eek*	**física** *fee-see-ka*	**fisica** *'fee-zee-ka*	**Physik** *fizeek*
biology	**la biologie** *la byol-o-jee*	**biología** *bee-oh-loh-ghee-a*	**biologia** *byoh-loh-'jee-a*	**Biologie** *bee-ologee*
computing	**l'informatique** *la(n)-for-ma-teek*	**informática** *een-fohr-ma-tee-ka*	**informatica** *een-for-'ma-tee-ka*	**Informatik** *informateek*

S	I	G
¿Qué estudias? *¿Keh ehs-too-dyas?*	**Cosa studi?** *'Koh-za 'stoo-dee?*	**Was studierst Du?** *Vass shtoodearst doo?*
¿Dónde puedo comprar libros de segunda mano? *¿Dohn-deh pweh-doh kohm-prar lee-brohs deh seh-goon-da ma-noh?*	**Dove si possono comprare i libri usati?** *'Doh-veh see 'pos-soh-noh-kom-'pra-reh ee 'lee-bree oo-'za-tee?*	**Wo kann ich gebrauchte Bücher kaufen?** *Vo kan ikh ge(r)browkhte(r) bewkher kow-fen?*
¿Cómo puedo inscribirme en la biblioteca? *¿Koh-moh pweh-doh eens-kree-beer-meh ehn la bee-blee-oh-teh-ka?*	**Come si fa per avere una tessera per la biblioteca?** *'Koh-meh see fa pehr a-'veh-reh oo-na 'tes-seh-ra pehr la bee-blyo-'teh-ka?*	**Wie bekomme ich eine Bibliothekskarte?** *Vee be(r)-komme(r) ikh eyne(r) bibliotakes-karte(r)?*

Useful words

	F	S	I	G
school	**une école** *ewn-eh-kol*	**un colegio, una escuela** *oon koh-lehgh-yoh, oo-na ehs-kweh-la*	**una scuola** *oona 'skwoh-la*	**eine Schule** *eyne(r) shoole(r)*
university	**l'université** *lew-nee-vair-seet-eh*	**la universidad** *la oo-nee-behr-see-da*	**l'università** *loo-nee-vehr-see-'ta*	**die Universität** *dee ooni-vairsi-tate*
lecture	**une conférence** *ewn ko(n)-fair-o(n)ss*	**una conferencia** *oo-na kohn-feh-rehn-thya*	**una conferenza** *oona kon-feh-'ren-tsa*	**eine Vorlesung** *eyne(r) for-layzoonk*
lesson	**un cours** *u(n) koor*	**una lección** *oo-na lehk-thyon*	**una lezione** *oona let-'tsyoh-neh*	**eine Stunde** *eyne(r) shtoonde(r)*
homework	**des devoirs** *deh de(r)-vwa(r)*	**deberes** *deh-beh-rehs*	**i compiti** *ee 'kom-pee-tee*	**Hausaufgaben** *house-owf-ga(r)ben*
essay	**une dissertation** *ewn dee-sair-ta-syo(n)*	**un trabajo escrito** *oon tra-ba-ghoh ehs-kree-toh*	**un tema** *oon 'teh-ma*	**ein Aufsatz** *eyn owf-zats*
translation	**une traduction** *ewn tra-dewk-syo(n)*	**una traducción** *oo-na tra-dook-thyon*	**una traduzione** *oona tra-doo-'tsyoh-neh*	**eine Übersetzung** *eyne(r) ewber-zetsoonk*
exam	**un examen** *un exama(n)*	**un examen** *oon ex-a-mehn*	**un esame** *oon e-'za-meh*	**eine Prüfung** *eyne(r) prewfoonk*
lecturer	**le prof, le maître de conférences** *le(r) prof, le(r) metr de(r) ko(n)-fair-o(n)ss*	**el/la profesor(-a)** *ehl/la proh-feh-sohr/sohra*	**il docente** *eel doh-'chen-teh*	**der Dozent/die Dozentin** *derr dotsent/dee dotsent-in*
teacher	**le professeur, le/la prof** *le(r) prof-essu(r), le(r)/la prof*	**el/la maestro(a)** *ehl/la ma-ehs-troh/tra*	**l'insegnante** *leen-sen-'nyan-teh*	**der Lehrer/die Lehrerin** *derr lairer/dee lairer-in*

Sightseeing

	F	S
Do you have any information on...?	**Est-ce que vous avez des informations sur...?** *Esske(r) voo-zavay dez-a(n)-for-ma-syo(n) syu(r)...?*	**¿Tiene información sobre...?** *¿Tyeh-neh een-fohr-ma-thyon soh-breh...?*
What is there to see here?	**Qu'est-ce qu'il y a à voir ici?** *Kess-kee-lya a vwa(r) ee-see?*	**¿Qué se debe visitar por aquí?** *¿Keh seh deh-beh bee-see-tar pohr a-kee?*
Are there any guided tours?	**Est-ce qu'il y a des visites guidées?** *Ess-kee-lya deh vizeet gee-deh?*	**¿Hay recorridos con guía?** *¿A-ee reh-koh-ree-dohs kohn gee-ya?*
Can I take photos?	**Est-ce que je peux prendre des photos?** *Esske(r) je(r) pe(r) pro(n)dr deh photo?*	**¿Puedo hacer fotos?** *¿Pweh-doh a-thehr foh-tohs?*

Things to see and do

	F	S	I	G
museum	**un musée** *u(n) mew-zeh*	**un museo** *oon moo-seh-oh*	**un museo** *oon moo-'zeh-oh*	**ein Museum** *eyn moozayoom*
palace	**un palais** *u(n) pal-leh*	**un palacio** *oon pa-la-thyoh*	**un palazzo** *oon pa-'lat-tsoh*	**ein Palast** *eyn palasst*
exhibition	**une exposition** *ewn expo-zissyo(n)*	**una exposición** *oo-na ex-poh-see-thyon*	**una mostra** *oona 'mos-tra*	**eine Ausstellung** *eyne(r) ows-shtelloonk*
church	**une église** *ewn eh-gleez*	**una iglesia** *oo-na ee-glehs-ya*	**una chiesa** *oona 'kyeh-za*	**eine Kirche** *eyne(r) keerkhe(r)*
festival	**une fête, un festival** *ewn fet, u(n) fes-tee-val*	**un festival** *oon fehs-tee-bal*	**un festival** *oon festival*	**ein Festival** *eyn festival*
castle	**un château** *u(n) sha-to*	**un castillo** *oon kas-teel-yoh*	**un castello** *oon kas-'tel-loh*	**ein Schloß** *eyn shloss*
boat trip	**une promenade en bateau** *ewn prome(r)-nahd o(n) ba-to*	**un paseo en barco** *oon pa-seh-oh ehn bar-koh*	**una gita in barca** *oona 'jee-ta een 'bar-ka*	**eine Bootsfahrt** *eyne(r) boots-fahrt*
art gallery	**un musée d'art** *u(n) mew-zeh dar*	**una galería de arte** *oo-na ga-leh-ree-a deh ar-teh*	**una galleria d'arte** *oona gal-leh-'ree-a 'dar-teh*	**eine Galerie** *eyne(r) galeree*
fair	**une foire** *ewn fwa(r)*	**una feria** *oo-na feh-rya*	**una fiera** *oona 'fyeh ra*	**ein Jahrmarkt** *eyn yar-markt*
vineyards	**des vignobles** *deh vee-nyo-bl*	**unos viñedos** *oo-nohs bee-nyeh-dos*	**i vigneti** *ee veen-'nyeh-tee*	**die Weinberge** *dee vine-bairge(r)*
caves	**des grottes** *deh grot*	**unas cuevas** *oo-nas kweh-bas*	**le grotte** *leh 'grot-teh*	**die Höhlen** *dee hu(r)len*

I	G
Mi può dare qualche informazione su . . . ? *Mee 'pwo 'da-reh 'kwal-keh een-for-ma-'tsyoh-neh soo . . . ?*	**Haben Sie Information über . . . ?** *Ha-ben zee informatseeon ewber . . . ?*
Cosa c'è da vedere qui? *'Koh-za 'cheh da veh-'deh-reh kwee?*	**Was gibt es hier zu sehen?** *Vass gipt ess heer tsoo zay-en?*
Ci sono visite guidate? *Chee 'soh-noh 'vee-zee-teh gwee-'da-teh?*	**Gibt es Führungen?** *Gipt ess fewroongen?*
Si possono fare fotografie? *See 'pos-soh-noh 'fah-reh foh-toh-gra-'fee-eh?*	**Darf ich fotografieren?** *Dahf ikh fotografeeren?*

Helpful words

	F	S	I	G
tourist office	**le Syndicat d'initiative** *le(r) sa(n)-dee-ka dee-nissya-teev*	**la Oficina de Información y Turismo** *la oh-fee-thee-na deh een-fohr-ma-thyon ee too-rees-moh*	**l'ufficio informazioni (turistiche)** *loof-'fee-choh een-for-ma-'tsyoh-nee (too-'ree-stee-keh)*	**das Fremdenverkehrs-amt** *dass fremden-fer-kairsamt*
restaurant guide	**un guide des restaurants** *u(n) geed deh restor-ra(n)*	**una guía de restaurantes** *oo-na gee-ya deh rehs-ta-oo-ran-tehs*	**una guida dei ristoranti** *oona 'gwee-da 'day-ee rees-toh-'ran-tee*	**ein Restaurantführer** *eyn restaurant-fewrer*
map of the area	**une carte de la région** *ewn kart de(r) la reh-jyo(n)*	**un mapa de la zona** *oon ma-pa deh la thoh-na*	**una piantina della zona** *oona pyan-'tee-na della 'zoh-na*	**eine Gebietskarte** *eyne(r) ge(r)beets-karte(r)*
town plan	**un plan de la ville** *u(n) plo(n) de(r) la veel*	**un plano de la ciudad** *oon pla-noh deh la th-yoo-da*	**una pianta della città** *oona 'pyan-ta della cheet-'ta*	**ein Stadtplan** *eyn shtaht-plan*
guide book	**un guide** *u(n) geed*	**una guía** *oo-na gee-ya*	**una guida turistica** *oona 'gwee-da too-'ree-stee-ka*	**ein Führer** *eyn fewrer*
bank holiday	**un jour férié** *u(n) joor fair-yeh*	**un día festivo** *oon dee-ya fehs-tee-boh*	**un giorno di festa nazionale** *oon 'johr-noh dee 'fes-ta na-tsyoh-'na-leh*	**ein Feiertag** *eyn fyer-tak*

Sports: what to do

	F	S	I	G
I like . . .	**J'aime . . .** *Jem . . .*	**Me gusta . . .** *Meh goos-ta . . .*	**Mi piace . . .** *Mee 'pya-cheh . . .*	**Ich gehe gern . . .** *Ikh gaye(r) gairn . .*
I don't like . . .	**Je n'aime pas . . .** *Je(r) nem pa . . .*	**No me gusta . . .** *Noh meh goos-ta . . .*	**Non mi piace . . .** *Non mee 'pya-cheh . . .*	**Ich gehe nicht gern . . .** *Ikh gaye(r) nikht gairn . . .*
. . . horse riding	**l'équitation** *lekkee-tassyo(n)*	**la equitación** *la eh-kee-ta-thyon*	**l'equitazione** *leh-kwee-ta-'tsyo-neh*	**reiten** *ryten*
. . . surfing	**le surf** *le(r) soorf*	**el surf** *ehl soorf*	**il surfing** *eel surfing*	**surfen** *soorfen*
. . . windsurfing	**la planche à voile** *la plo(n)sh a vwal*	**el windsurfing** *ehl weend-soor-feen*	**il windsurf** *eel windsurf*	**zum Windsurfen** *tsoom vint-soorfen*
. . . sailing	**faire de la voile** *fair de(r) la vwal*	**la navegación a vela** *la na-beh-ga-thyon a beh-la*	**la vela** *la 'veh-la*	**segeln** *say-gln*
. . . hang gliding	**le deltaplane** *le(r) deltaplane*	**el vuelo con ala delta** *ehl bweh-loh kohn ala dehl-ta*	**il deltaplano** *eel del-ta-'pla-noh*	**zum Drachenfliegen** *tsoom drakhen-fleegen*
. . . water skiing	**le ski nautique** *le(r) skee no-teek*	**el esquí acuático** *ehl ehs-kee a-kwa-tee-koh*	**lo sci d'acqua** *lo shee 'dak-kwa*	**Wasserski laufen** *vasser-ski lowfen*
. . . climbing	**l'escalade** *less-kalahd*	**el alpinismo** *ehl alpee-nees-moh*	**l'alpinismo** *lal-pee-'neez-moh*	**bergsteigen** *bairg-shty-gen*
. . . cycling	**le cyclisme** *le(r) see-klee-sm*	**el ciclismo** *ehl thee-klees-moh*	**il ciclismo** *eel chee-'cleez-moh*	**radfahren** *raht-fahren*
. . . jogging	**le jogging** *le(r) jogging*	**el footing** *ehl foo-teen*	**lo jogging** *lo jogging*	**joggen** *yoggen*
. . . canoeing	**faire du canoë** *fair dew kano-eh*	**el piragüismo** *ehl pee-ra-gwees-moh*	**andare in canoa** *an-'da-reh een 'ka-'noh-a*	**Kanufahren** *kanoo-fahren*
. . . swimming	**la natation** *la na-tassyo(n)*	**la natación** *la na-ta-thyon*	**il nuoto** *eel 'nwoh-toh*	**schwimmen** *shvimmen*
. . . (scuba) diving	**la plongée** *la plo(n)-jeh*	**el submarinismo** *ehl soob-ma-ree-nees-moh*	**l'immersione (a grande profondità)** *leem-mair-see-'oh-neh (a 'gran-deh pro-fon-dee-'ta)*	**tauchen** *taw-khen*

	F	S	I	G
I play...	**Je joue au...** *Je(r) joo o...*	**Juego al...** *Ghweh-goh al...*	**Gioco a...** *'Joh-koh a...*	**Ich spiele...** *Ikh shpeele(r)...*
I don't play...	**Je ne joue pas au...** *Je(r) ne(r) joo pa o...*	**No juego al...** *Noh ghweh-goh al...*	**Non sò giocare a...** *Non soh joh-'ka-reh a...*	**Ich spiele nicht...** *Ikh shpeele(r) nikht...*
...tennis	**tennis** *ten-neess*	**tenis** *teh-nees*	**tennis** *tennis*	**Tennis** *tennis*
...badminton	**badminton** *badminton*	**badminton** *bad-meen-tohn*	**badminton** *badminton*	**Federball** *fayder-bal*
...squash	**squash** *squash*	**squash** *skwa-sh*	**squash** *squash*	**Squash** *squash*
...soccer	**football** *foot-bal*	**fútbol** *foot-bohl*	**calcio, football** *'kal-cho, football*	**Fußball** *fooss-bal*
...rugby	**rugby** *rugby*	**rugby** *roog-bee*	**rugby** *rugby*	**Rugby** *rugby*
...basketball	**basket** *basket*	**baloncesto** *ba-lohn-thehs-toh*	**pallacanestro** *pal-la-ka-'nes-troh*	**Basketball** *basket-bal*
...volleyball	**volley** *volley*	**balonvolea** *ba-lohn-boh-leh-a*	**pallavolo** *pal-la-'voh-loh*	**Volleyball** *volley-bal*
...table tennis	**ping-pong** *ping-pong*	**tenis de mesa, ping-pong** *teh-nees deh meh-sa, peen pohn*	**tennis da tavolo, ping-pong** *tennis da 'ta-voh-loh, ping-pong*	**Tischtennis** *tish-tennis*
...cricket	**cricket** *kree-ket*	**cricket** *kree-keht*	**cricket** *cricket*	**Kricket** *kriket*

Helpful words

	F	S	I	G
sports centre	**le centre sportif** *le(r) so(n)tr spor-teef*	**un centro de deportes** *un thehn-troh deh deh-pohr-tehs*	**il centro sportivo** *eel 'chen-troh spor-'tee-voh*	**ein Sportzentrum** *eyn shport-tsentroom*
swimming pool	**la piscine** *la pee-seen*	**la piscina** *la pee-thee-na*	**la piscina** *la pee-'shee-na*	**ein Schwimmbad** *eyn shvim-baht*
beach	**la plage** *la plahj*	**la playa** *la pla-ya*	**la spiaggia** *la 'spyaj-ja*	**der Strand** *derr shtrant*
match	**un match** *u(n) match*	**un partido** *oon par-tee-doh*	**una partita** *oona par-'tee-ta*	**ein Spiel** *eyn shpeel*
game	**une partie** *ewn par-tee*	**una partida** *oo-na par-tee-da*	**una partita** *oona par-'tee-ta*	**ein Spiel** *eyn shpeel*

Sports: lessons and equipment

	F	S
Can we book a court?	**On peut réserver un court?** *O(n) pe(r) reh-zair-veh u(n) koor?*	**¿Podemos alquilar una pista?** *¿Poh-deh-mohs al-kee-lar oo-na pees-ta?*
Can we hire equipment?	**On peut louer le matériel?** *O(n) pe(r) looweh le(r) ma-teh-ryel?*	**¿Podemos alquilar el equipo?** *¿Poh-deh-mohs al-kee-lar ehl eh-kee-poh?*
I am a beginner.	**Je suis un débutant/une débutante.** *Je(r) swee u(n) deh-bew-to(n)/ ewn deh-bew-to(n)te(r).*	**Soy un/una principiante.** *Soh-ee oon/oo-na preen-theep-yan-teh.*
Can I get lessons?	**Je peux prendre des leçons?** *Je(r) pe(r) pro(n)dr deh le(r)sso(n)?*	**¿Podría recibir lecciones?** *¿Poh-dree-a reh-thee-beer lehk-thyon-ehs?*
rackets	**des raquettes** *deh ra-ket*	**unas raquetas** *oo-nas ra-keh-tas*
ball	**une balle[1]/un ballon[2]** *ewn bal/u(n) balo(n)*	**una pelota** *oo-na peh-loh-tah*

[1] This is used for a small ball. [2] This is used for a large ball.

On the slopes

	F	S	I	G
skis	**des skis** *deh skee*	**unos esquís** *oo-nohs ehs-kees*	**gli sci** *lee shee*	**die Skier** *dee skee-er*
boots	**des chaussures de ski** *deh sho-syoor de(r) skee*	**unas botas** *oo-nas boh-tas*	**gli scarponi** *lee scar-'poh-nee*	**die Stiefel** *dee shtee-fel*
ski pass	**un forfait** *u(n) fo(r)-feh*	**un pase de esqui** *oon pa-seh deh ehs-kee*	**un abbonamento, lo ski pass** *oon ab-boh-na-'men-toh, loh ski pass*	**eine Liftkarte** *eyne(r) lift-karte(r)*
chair lift	**le télésiège** *le(r) teh-leh-syairj*	**el telesilla** *ehl teh-leh-see-lya*	**la seggiovia** *la sej-joh-'vee-a*	**der Sessellift** *derr zessel-lift*
drag lift	**le téléski** *le(r) teh-leh-skee*	**ehl telearrastre, el telesquí** *ehl teh-leh-aras-treh, ehl teh-lehs-kee*	**la sciovia, lo ski-lift** *la shee-oh-'vee-a, loh ski-lift*	**der Schlepplift** *derr shlep-lift*
ski goggles	**des lunettes de ski** *deh lew-net de(r) skee*	**unas gafas de esquí** *oo-nas ga-fas deh ehs-kee*	**gli occhiali da sci** *lee ok-'kya-lee da shee*	**eine Skibrille** *eyne(r) ski-brille(r)*

I	G
Possiamo prenotare il campo per una partita? *Pos-'sya-moh preh-noh-'ta-reh eel 'kam-poh pehr oona par-'tee-ta?*	**Können wir einen Platz reservieren?** *Ku(r)nen veer eynen platz rezer-veeren?*
Possiamo noleggiare l'equipaggiamento? *Pos-'sya-moh noh-lehj-'ja-reh leh-kwee-paj-ja-'men-toh?*	**Können wir die Ausrüstung leihen?** *Ku(r)nen veer dee owss-rewstoong lyen?*
Sono principiante. *'Soh-noh preen-chee-'pyan-teh.*	**Ich bin Anfänger.** *Ikh bin an-fenger.*
Si possono prendere lezioni? *See 'pos-soh-noh 'pren-deh-reh let-'tsyoh-nee?*	**Kann ich Stunden nehmen?** *Kan ikh shtoonden nay-men?*
le racchette *leh rak-'ket-teh*	**die Schläger** *dee shlay-ger*
una palla[1]/un pallone[2] *oona 'pal-la/oon pal-'loh-neh*	**ein Ball** *eyn bal*

Water sports

	F	S	I	G
mask	**un masque** *u(n) massk*	**unas gafas de buceo** *oo-nas ga-fas deh boo-theh-oh*	**una maschera** *oona 'mas-keh-ra*	**eine Tauchermaske** *eyne(r) towkhe(r)-maske(r)*
snorkel	**un tuba** *u(n) tewba*	**un tubo** *oon too-boh*	**un respiratore** *oon res-pee-ra-'toh-reh*	**ein Schnorchel** *eyn shnor-kel*
flippers	**des palmes** *deh pal-m*	**unas aletas** *oo-nas a-leh-tas*	**le pinne** *leh 'peen-neh*	**die Schwimmflossen** *dee shvim-flossen*
wetsuit	**une combinaison de plongée** *ewn ko(m)-bee-neh-zo(n) de(r) plo(n)-jeh*	**un traje de bucear** *oon tra-gheh deh boo-theh-ar*	**una tuta subacquea** *oona 'too-ta soob-ak-'kweh-a*	**ein Taucheranzug** *eyn towkhe(r)-an-tsook*
life jacket	**un gilet de sauvetage** *u(n) jee-leh de(r) so-v-tahj*	**un salvavidas** *oon sal-ba-bee-das*	**un giubbotto di salvataggio** *oon joob-'bot-toh dee sal-va-'taj-joh*	**eine Schwimmweste** *eyne(r) shvim-veste(r)*
surfboard	**une planche de surf** *ewn plo(n)sh de(r) syoorf*	**una tabla de surf** *oo-na ta-bla deh soorf*	**un surf, una tavola per il surf** *oon surf, oona 'ta-voh-la pehr eel surf*	**ein Surfbrett** *eyn soorf-bret*
boat	**un bateau** *u(n) bat-o*	**una barca** *oo-na bar-ka*	**una barca** *oona 'bar-ka*	**ein Boot** *eyn boot*

A night out

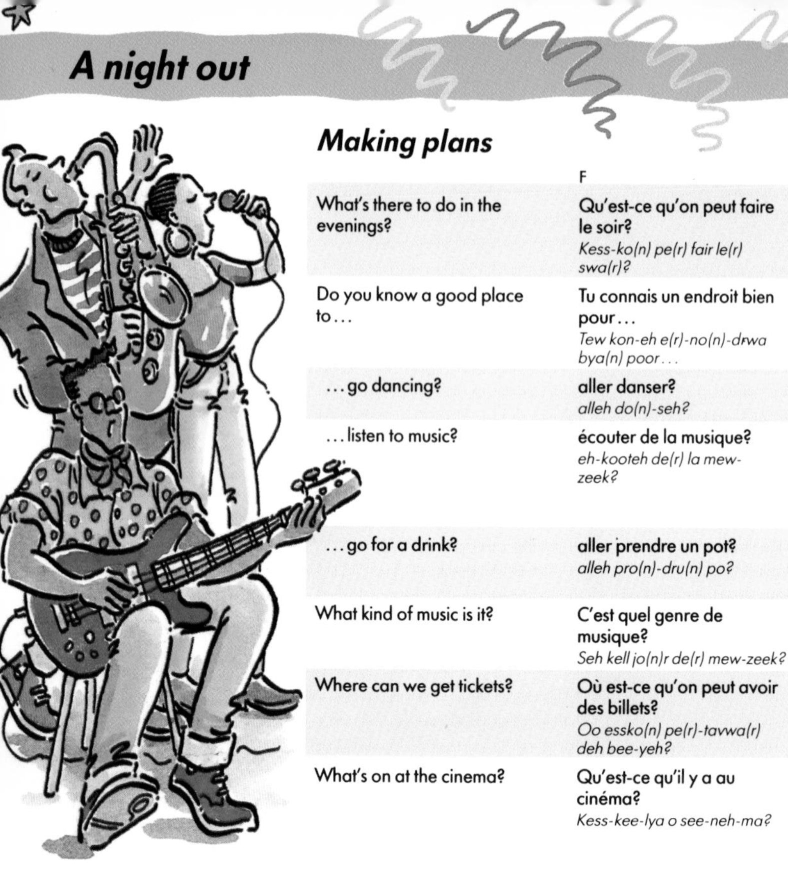

Making plans

	F
What's there to do in the evenings?	**Qu'est-ce qu'on peut faire le soir?** *Kess-ko(n) pe(r) fair le(r) swa(r)?*
Do you know a good place to...	**Tu connais un endroit bien pour...** *Tew kon-eh e(r)-no(n)-drwa bya(n) poor...*
...go dancing?	**aller danser?** *alleh do(n)-seh?*
...listen to music?	**écouter de la musique?** *eh-kooteh de(r) la mew-zeek?*
...go for a drink?	**aller prendre un pot?** *alleh pro(n)-dru(n) po?*
What kind of music is it?	**C'est quel genre de musique?** *Seh kell jo(n)r de(r) mew-zeek?*
Where can we get tickets?	**Où est-ce qu'on peut avoir des billets?** *Oo essko(n) pe(r)-tavwa(r) deh bee-yeh?*
What's on at the cinema?	**Qu'est-ce qu'il y a au cinéma?** *Kess-kee-lya o see-neh-ma?*

Entertainments

	F	S	I	G
film	**un film** *u(n) feelm*	**una película** *oo-na peh-lee-koo-la*	**un film** *oon feelm*	**ein Film** *eyn feelm*
theatre	**le théâtre** *le(r) teh-ahtr*	**el teatro** *ehl teh-a-troh*	**il teatro** *eel teh-'a-troh*	**das Theater** *dass tay-ahter*
concert	**un concert** *u(n) ko(n)-sair*	**un concierto** *oon kohn-thyehr-toh*	**un concerto** *oon kon-'cher-toh*	**ein Konzert** *eyn kon-tsairt*
disco	**une boîte, une discothèque** *ewn bwat, ewn dee-sko-tek*	**una discoteca** *oo-na dees-koh-teh-ka*	**una discoteca** *oona dees-koh-'teh-ka*	**eine Disco** *eyne(r) disco*
party	**une fête** *ewn fet*	**una fiesta** *oo-na fyehs-ta*	**una festa** *oona 'fes-ta*	**eine Fete** *eyne(r) fate*
nightclub	**une boîte (de nuit)** *ewn bwat (de(r) nwee)*	**un club nocturno, una disco** *oon kloob nohk-toor-noh, oo-na dees-koh*	**un locale notturno, un night** *oon loh-'ka-leh not-'toor-noh, oon 'na-eet*	**eine Bar, eine Disco** *eyne(r) bar, eyne(r) disco*

S	I	G
¿Qué se puede hacer por las noches? *¿Keh seh pweh-deh a-thehr pohr las noh-tchehs?*	**Cosa si può fare la sera?** *'Koh-za see 'pwo 'fa-reh la 'seh-ra?*	**Was kann man abends machen?** *Vass kan man ah-bents mah-khen?*
¿Sabes de un buen sitio para . . . *¿Sa-behs deh oon bwehn seet-yoh pa-ra . . .*	**Conosci un buon locale per. . .** *Koh-'noh-shee oon boo-'on loh-'ka-leh pehr. . .*	**Wo kann man gut . . .** *Vo kan man goot . . .*
ir a bailar? *eer a ba-ee-lar?*	**andare a ballare?** *an-'da-reh a bal-'la-reh?*	**tanzen gehen?** *tan-tsen gayen?*
escuchar música? *ehs-koo-tchar moo-see-ka?*	**andare ad ascoltare un po'di musica?** *an-'da-reh ad as-kol-'ta-reh oon 'poh dee 'moo-zee-ka?*	**Musik hören?** *moo-zeek hu(r)en?*
ir de copas? *eer deh koh-pas?*	**andare a bere qualcosa?** *an-'da-reh a 'beh-reh kwal-'koh-za?*	**etwas trinken gehen?** *et-vass trinken gayen?*
¿Qué clase de música es? *¿Keh kla-seh deh moo-see-ka ehs?*	**Che tipo di musica è?** *Keh 'tee-poh dee 'moo-zee-ka eh?*	**Was ist das für Musik?** *Vass isst dass fewr moo-zeek?*
¿Dónde podemos conseguir entradas? *¿Dohn-deh poh-deh-mohs kohn-seh-geer ehn-tra-das?*	**Dove si comprano i biglietti?** *'Doh-veh see 'kom-pra-noh ee beel-'lyet-tee?*	**Wo bekommt man Karten?** *Vo be(r)-komt man karten?*
¿Qué película hacen? *¿Keh peh-lee-koo-la a-thehn?*	**Cosa danno al cinema?** *'Koh-za 'dan-noh al 'chee-neh-ma?*	**Was läuft im Kino?** *Vass loyft im kee-no?*

Music

	F	S	I	G
jazz	le jazz *le(r) jazz*	el jazz *ehl djas*	il jazz *eel jazz*	der Jazz *derr jazz*
blues	le blues *le(r) blooz*	el blues *ehl bloos*	il blues *eel blooz*	der Blues *derr blooz*
reggae	le reggae *le(r) reggay*	el reggae *ehl reh-geh*	il reggae *eel 'reg-geh*	der Reggae *derr regay*
heavy metal	le heavy metal *le(r) eh-vee metal*	el heavy metal *ehl eh-bee meh-tal*	l'heavy metal *'leh-vee metal*	die Heavy Metal *dee heavy metal*
rock	le rock *le(r) rock*	el rock *ehl rohk*	il rock *eel rock*	der Rock *derr rock*
pop	la musique pop *la mew-zeek pop*	el pop *ehl pohp*	la musica pop *la 'moo-zee-ka pop*	der Pop *derr pop*
classical	la musique classique *la mew-zeek kla-seek*	la música clásica *la moo-see-ka kla-see-ka*	la musica classica *la 'moo--zee-ka 'klas-see-ka*	die klassische Musik *dee klassishe(r) moo-zeek*
soul	la musique soul *la mew-zeek soul*	el soul *ehl soh-ool*	il soul *eel soul*	der Soul *derr soul*

Meeting people

Making friends

	F	S
What's your name?	Comment tu t'appelles? *Ko-mo(n) tew ta-pell?*	¿Cómo te llamas? *¿Koh-moh teh lya-mas?*
Where are you from?	Tu es d'où? *Tew eh doo?*	¿De dónde eres? *¿Deh dohn-deh eh-rehs?*
How old are you?	Tu as quel âge? *Tew-a kell-ahj?*	¿Cuántos años tienes? *¿Kwan-tohs a-nyohs tyeh-nehs?*
What's your address?	Quelle est ton adresse? *Kelleh tonadress?*	¿Cuál es tu dirección? *¿Kwal ehs too dee-rehk-thyon?*
Do you want a drink?	Tu veux boire quelque chose? *Tew ve(r) bwa(r) kellke(r) sho-z?*	¿Quieres beber algo? *¿Kyeh-rehs beh-behr al-goh?*
Do you want to dance?	Tu veux danser? *Tew ve(r) do(n)-seh?*	¿Quieres bailar? *¿Kyeh-rehs ba-ee-lar?*
Can I see you again?	On peut se revoir? *O(n) pe(r) se(r) re(r)-vwa(r)?*	¿Podemos vernos otra vez? *¿Poh-deh-mos behr-nohs oh-tra beh-th?*
Where shall we meet?	Où est-ce qu'on se retrouve? *Oo-essko(n) se(r) re(r)-troov?*	¿Dónde nos encontramos? *¿Dohn-deh nohs ehn-kohn-tra-mohs?*

Talking about yourself

	F	S	I	G
My name is...	Je m'appelle... *Je(r) ma-pell...*	Me llamo... *Meh lya-moh...*	Mi chiamo... *Mee 'kya-moh...*	Ich heiße... *Ikh hysse(r)...*
I come from...	Je viens de... *Je(r) vya(n) de(r)*	Soy de... *So-ee deh...*	Vengo da... *'Ven-goh da...*	Ich komme aus... *Ikh komme(r) owss...*
I'm seventeen.[1]	J'ai dix-sept ans. *Jeh dee-set-o(n).*	Tengo diecisiete años. *Tehn-goh dyeh-thee-syeh-teh a-nyohs.*	Ho diciassette anni. *O dee-chas-'set-teh 'an-nee.*	Ich bin siebzehn. *Ikh bin zeeb-tsayn.*

[1] See pages 78-81 for numbers.

I	G
Come ti chiami? *'Koh-meh tee 'kya-mee?*	Wie heißt du? *Vee hy-sst doo?*
Da dove vieni? *Da 'doh-veh 'vyeh-nee?*	Woher kommst du? *Voe-hair komst doo?*
Quanti anni hai? *'Kwan-tee 'an-nee 'a-ee?*	Wie alt bist du? *Vee alt bisst doo?*
Qual è il tuo indirizzo? *'Kwa-leh eel too-'o een-dee-'reet-tsoh?*	Wo wohnst du? *Voe vohnst doo?*
Vuoi bere qualcosa? *'Vwoy 'beh-reh kwal-'koh-za?*	Willst du etwas trinken? *Villst doo etvass trinken?*
Vuoi ballare? *'Vwoy bal-'la-reh?*	Hast du Lust zu tanzen? *Hasst doo loost tsoo tan-tsen?*
Ci possiamo rivedere? *Chee pos-'sya-moh ree-veh-'deh-reh?*	Können wir uns mal treffen? *Ku(r)nen veer oonss mal treffen?*
Dove ci vediamo? *'Doh-veh chee veh-'dya-moh?*	Wo treffen wir uns? *Voe treffen veer oonss?*

Gossiping

	F
I don't know anyone here.	Je ne connais personne ici. *Je(r) ne(r) konneh pair-son ee-see.*
Who's that?	Qui est-ce? *Kee-ess?*
I'd like to meet...	Je voudrais rencontrer... *Je(r) voo-dreh ro(n)-ko(n)-treh...*
Do you know Helen?	Tu connais Helen? *Tew konneh ell-en?*
What's she like?	Elle est comment? *Ell eh kommo(n)?*
Carl got off with Anna.	Carl a une touche* avec Anna. *Karl a ewn toosh-avek anna.*
Jo's going out with Luke.	Jo sort avec Luke. *Jo sor avek Lewk.*
We had a row.	On s'est disputé. *O(n) seh deess-pew-teh.*
He/she kissed me.	Il/elle m'a embrassé(-e). *Eel/ell ma o(m)-bra-seh.*

Handy words

	F	S	I	G
He/she is...	Il/elle est... *Eel/ell eh...*	El/ella es... *Ehl/ehl-ya ehs...*	Lui/lei è... *'Loo-ee/lay eh...*	Er/sie ist... *Air/zee isst...*
tall	grand/grande *gro(n)/gro(n)d*	alto/alta *al-toh/al-ta*	alto/alta *'al-toh/'al-ta*	groß *gross*
short	petit/petite *pe(r)-tee/pe(r)-teet*	bajo/baja *ba-ghoh/ba-gha*	basso/bassa *'bas-soh/'bas-sa*	klein *kline*
thin	mince *ma(n)ss*	delgado/delgada *dehl-ga-doh/dehl-ga-da*	magro/magra *'mag-roh/'mag-ra*	dünn *dewn*
fat	gros/grosse *gro/gross*	gordo/gorda *gohr-doh/gohr-dah*	grasso/grassa *'gras-soh/'gras-sa*	dick *dick*
fair	blond/blonde *blo(n)/blo(n)d*	rubio/rubia *roo-byoh/roo-bya*	biondo/bionda *'byon-doh/'byon-da*	hell *hell*
dark	brun/brune *bru(n)/brewn*	moreno/morena *moh-reh-noh/moh-reh-na*	bruno/bruna *'broo-noh/'broo-na*	dunkel *doonkel*
good-looking	beau/belle *bo/bell*	guapo/guapa *gwa-poh/gwa-pa*	bello/bella *'bel-loh-/'bel-la*	gutaussehend *goot-owss-zayend*

* Slang.

S	I	G
No conozco a nadie aquí. *Noh koh-noh-th-koh a na-dyeh a-kee.*	**Non conosco nessuno qui.** *Non koh-'nos-koh nes-'soon-oh kwee.*	**Ich kenne hier niemanden.** *Ikh kenne(r) heer nee-manden.*
¿Quién es aquél/aquélla? *¿Kyehn ehs a-kehl/a-kehl-ya?*	**Chi è quella/quello?** *Kee eh 'kwel-la/'kwel-lo?*	**Wer ist das?** *Vair isst dass?*
Me gustaría conocer a ... *Meh goos-ta-ree-a koh-noh-thehr a ...*	**Vorrei conoscere ...** *Vor-'ray koh-'noh-sheh-reh ...*	**Ich möchte gern ... kennenlernen.** *Ikh mu(r)khte(r) gairn ... kennen-lairnen.*
¿Conoces a Helen? *¿Koh-noh-thehs a eh-lehn?*	**Conosci Helen?** *Ko-'noh-shee 'ay-len?*	**Kennst du Helen?** *Kennst doo helen?*
¿Cómo es? *¿Koh-moh ehs?*	**Che tipo è?** *Keh 'tee-po eh?*	**Wie ist sie?** *Vee isst zee?*
Carl ligó con Anna. *Karl lee-goh kohn an-na.*	**Carl sta andando dietro a Anna.** *'Karl sta an-'da-doh dyeh-troh a 'an-na.*	**Carl hat Anna aufgerissen*.** *Karl haht anna owf-ge(r)-rissen.*
Jo sale con Luke. *Dj-oh sa-leh kohn look.*	**Jo e Luke stanno insieme.** *Jo eh 'look 'stan-noh een-'syeh-meh.*	**Jo geht mit Luke.** *Jo gayt mit luke.*
Tuvimos una pelea. *Too-bee-mohs oo-na peh-leh-a.*	**Abbiamo litigato.** *Ab-'bya-moh lee-tee-'ga-toh.*	**Wir haben uns gestritten.** *Veer hah-ben oonss ge(r)-shtritten.*
Me besó. *Meh beh-soh.*	**Mi ha dato un bacio.** *Mee a 'da-toh oon ba-cho.*	**Er/Sie hat mich geküßt.** *Air/zee hat mikh ge(r)-kewsst.*

	F	S	I	G
ugly	**laid/laide, moche*** *leh/led, mosh*	**feo/fea** *feh-oh/feh-a*	**brutto/brutta** *'broot-toh/'broot-ta*	**häßlich** *hesslikh*
nice, ok	**sympa** *sa(m)-pa*	**simpático/ simpática** *seem-pa-tee-koh/ seem-pa-tee-ka*	**simpatico/ simpatica** *seem-'pa-tee-koh/ seem-'pa-tee-ka*	**nett** *net*
horrible, nasty	**mauvais/ mauvaise, vache*** *mo-veh/mo-vez, vash*	**horrible** *oh-ree-bleh*	**antipatico/ antipatica** *an-tee-'pa-tee-koh/an-tee-'pa-tee-ka*	**gemein** *ge(r)-mine*
trendy	**branché/ branchée*** *bro(n)-sheh/bro(n)-sheh*	**al día**[1] *al dee-a*	**alla moda** *al-la moh-da*	**immer vornedran, in** *immer forne(r)-dran, in*
old-fashioned, square	**ringard/ringarde*** *ra(n)-gar/ra(n)-gard*	**anticuado/ anticuado** *an-tee-kwa-doh/ an-tee-kwa-da*	**all'antica** *al-lan-'tee-ka*	**altmodisch, out** *alt-modish, out*

[1] Use with *estar*. See page 68.

Slang and everyday expressions

	F
How's it going?	**Comment ça va?** *Kommo(n) sa va?*
All right.	**Pas mal.** *Pa mal.*
This is boring.	**Qu'est-ce que c'est rasoir*.** *Kesske(r) seh ra-zwar.*
Yep, I agree.	**Ouais, d'accord.** *Weh, da-ko(r).*
Shut up!	**La ferme*!** *La fairm!*
See you soon.	**A bientôt.** *A byan-to.*
I'll give you a ring.	**Je te passerai un coup de fil.** *Je(r) te(r) passer-eh u(n) koo de(r) feel.*
Hurry up!	**Dépêche-toi!** *Deh-pesh twa!*
See you some time.	**A un de ces jours.** *A u(n) de(r) seh joor.*
You're joking.	**Tu blagues.** *Tew blahg.*

Handy words

	F	S	I	G
OK	**OK, bien** *ok, bya(n)*	**vale** *ba-leh*	**OK** *ok*	**nett** *net*
very, completely	**hyper, super, vachement*** *ee-pair, syoo-pair, vash-mo(n)*	**super-, hiper-, ultra-** *soo-pehr-, ee-pehr-, ool-tra-*	**proprio, veramente** *'proh-pryoh, veh-ra-'men-teh*	**absolut, irre, total, echt** *apsoloot, irre(r), toe-tal, ekht*
great, brilliant	**super, terrible, chouette*** *syoo-pair, tairee-bl, shwet*	**guay*[1], superguay*[1], bestial*[1]** *gwa-ee, soo-pehr-gwa-ee, behs-t-yal*	**benissimo, perfetto** *be-'nees-see-moh, pehr-'fet-toh*	**toll, spitzenmäßig, ultra, fetzig** *toll, shpitsen-messikh, ooltra, fetsikh*
boyfriend	**le Jules**** *le(r) jool*	**el chico*** *ehl tchee-koh*	**il ragazzo** *eel ra-'gat-tsoh*	**der Alte**** *derr alte*
girlfriend	**la nana**** *la nana*	**la chica*, la niña*** *la tchee-ka, la nee-nya*	**la ragazza** *la ra-'gat-tsa*	**die Alte**** *dee alte*

S	I	G
¿Cómo van las cosas? *¿Koh-moh ban las koh-sas?*	**Come va?** *'Koh-meh va?*	**Wie geht's?** *Vee gaytss?*
Bien. *Byehn.*	**Bene.** *'Beh-neh.*	**Alles klar.** *A-less klar.*
Esto es aburridísimo. *Ehs-toh ehs a-boo-ree-dee-see-moh.*	**Che noia / che palle**.** *Keh 'noh-ya / keh 'pal-leh.*	**Das geht mir auf den Keks*.** *Dass gayt meer owf den keks.*
Vale. *Ba-leh.*	**Sì, sono d'accordo.** *See, 'so-noh dak-'kor-doh.*	**Ich bin deiner Meinung.** *Ikh bin diner my-noong.*
¡Cállate! *Ka-lya-teh!*	**Sta zitto(a)!** *Sta 'tsee-toh/ta!*	**Halt den Mund*!** *Halt den moont!*
Hasta luego. *As-ta lweh-goh.*	**A presto.** *A 'pres-toh.*	**Bis bald.** *Biss balt.*
Te llamaré. *Teh lya-ma-reh.*	**Ti do un colpo di telefono.** *Tee doh oon 'kol-poh dee teh-'leh-foh-noh.*	**Ich ruf' dich an.** *Ikh roof dikh an.*
¡Date prisa! *Da-teh pree-sa!*	**Sbrigati!** *'Sbree-ga-tee!*	**Beeil dich!** *Be(r)-ile dikh!*
Hasta pronto. *As-ta prohn-toh.*	**Ci vediamo.** *Chee veh-dya-moh.*	**Wir sehen uns.** *Veer zayen oonss.*
Bromeas. *Broh-meh-as.*	**Ma scherzi!** *Ma 'skehr-tsee!*	**Mach keine Witze.** *Makh kine(r) vit-tse(r).*

	F	S	I	G
money, dough	**des sous, du fric*** *deh soo, dew freek*	**tela*, pasta*** *teh-la, pas-ta*	**soldi, grana** *'sol-dee, 'gra-na*	**Kies*, Knete*, Kohle*** *keess, knete(r), koe-le(r)*
food, grub	**la bouffe*** *la boof*	**el papeo*** *ehl pa-peh-oh*	**cibo, da mangiare** *'chee-boh, da man-'ja-reh*	**Futter** *footer*
friend, mate	**un pote*, un copain/une copine** *u(n) poat, u(n) kopa(n)/ewn kopeen*	**un/una colega*** *oon/oo-na koh-leh-ga*	**un amico/una amica** *oon a-'mee-ko/ oona a-'mee-ka*	**ein Kumpel** *eyn koompel*

* Slang. ** Rude. [1] Use with *ser* or *estar*. See page 68.

Doctors and dentists

	F	S
I want to see...	**Je voudrais voir...** *Je(r) voo-dreh vwar...*	**Quiero ver...** *Kyeh-roh behr...*
...a doctor	**un médecin** *u(n) medsa(n)*	**un médico** *oon meh-dee-koh*
...a dentist	**un dentiste** *u(n) do(n)-teest*	**un dentista** *oon dehn-tees-ta*
...a woman doctor	**une femme docteur** *ewn fam dok-tu(r)*	**una médica** *oo-na meh-dee-ka*
Do you have anything for...?	**Est-ce que vous avez quelque chose pour...** *Esske(r) voo-zaveh kellke(r) sho-z poor...*	**¿Tiene algo para...?** *¿Tyeh-neh al-goh pa-ra...?*

At the doctor's

	F	S	I	G
I have...	**J'ai...** *Jeh...*	**Tengo** *Tehn-goh...*	**Ho...** *O...*	**Ich habe...** *Ikh hah-be(r)*
...toothache	**mal aux dents** *mal o do(n)*	**dolor de muelas** *doh-lohr deh mweh-las*	**mal di denti** *mal dee 'den-tee*	**Zahnschmerzen** *tsahn-shmair-tsen*
...a temperature	**de la température** *de(r) la to(m)-paira-tew-r*	**fiebre** *fyeh-breh*	**la febbre** *la 'feb-breh*	**Fieber** *feeber*
...a sore throat	**mal à la gorge** *mal a la gorj*	**dolor de garganta** *doh-lohr deh gar-gan-ta*	**mal di gola** *mal dee 'goh-la*	**Halsschmerzen** *halss-shmairtsen*
...diarrhea	**la diarrhée** *la dya-reh*	**diarrea** *dee-a-reh-a*	**la diarrea** *la dyar-'reh-a*	**Durchfall** *doorkh-fal*
...sunstroke	**attrapé(e) une insolation** *a-tra-peh ew-na(n)-sol-asyo(n)*	**una insolación** *oo-na een-soh-la-thyon*	**preso un colpo di sole** *'preh-soh oon 'kol-poh dee 'soh-leh*	**einen Hitzschlag** *eynen hits-shlahg*
...a headache	**mal à la tête** *mal a la tet*	**dolor de cabeza** *doh-lohr- deh ka-beh-tha*	**mal di testa** *mal dee 'tes-ta*	**Kopfschmerzen** *kopf-shmairtsen*
...a stomach ache	**mal au ventre** *mal o vo(n)-tr*	**dolor de estómago** *doh-lohr deh ehs-toh-ma-goh*	**mal di stomaco** *mal dee 'stoh-ma-koh*	**Bauchschmerzen** *bowkh-shmairtsen*
...my period	**mes règles** *meh reh-gl*	**el período** *ehl peh-ree-oh-doh*	**le mestruazioni** *leh mes-troo-a-'tsyoh-nee*	**meine Tage** *mine(r) tahge(r)*
...a cold	**un rhume** *u(n) rew-m*	**un resfriado** *oon rehs-free-a-doh*	**il raffreddore** *eel raf-fred-'doh-reh*	**eine Erkältung** *eyne(r) air-keltoong*
...flu	**la grippe** *la greep*	**una gripe** *oona gree-peh*	**l'influenza** *leen-floo-'ayn-za*	**eine Grippe** *eyne(r) grippe(r)*

I	G
Vorrei farmi vedere da . . . *Vor-'ray 'far-mee veh-'deh-reh da . . .*	**Ich will . . .** *Ikh vill . . .*
un medico *oon 'meh-dee-koh*	**zum Arzt** *tsoom artst*
un dentista *oon den-'tee-sta*	**zum Zahnarzt** *tsoom tsahn-artst*
una dottoressa *oona dot-toh-'res-sa*	**zu einer Ärztin** *tsoo eyner airts-tin*
Ha qualcosa per . . . ? *A kwal-'koh-za pehr . . . ?*	**Haben Sie etwas gegen . . .** *Hah-ben zee et-vass gaygen . . .*

	F	S	I	G
I've been bitten[1].	**J'ai été mordu(-e).** *Jeh eteh mor-dew.*	**Tengo una mordedura.** *Tehn-goh oo-na mohr-deh-doo-ra.*	**Sono stato(a) morso(a).** *'Soh-noh 'sta-toh/ta 'mor-soh/sa.*	**Mich hat etwas gebissen.** *Mikh hat et-vass ge(r)-bissen.*
I've been sick.	**J'ai vomi.** *Jeh vomee.*	**He vomitado.** *Eh boh-mee-ta-doh.*	**Ho vomitato.** *Oh vo-mee-'ta-toh.*	**Ich mußte mich übergeben.** *Ikh moosste(r) mikh ewber-gayben.*
I've been stung.	**J'ai été piqué(-e).** *Jeh eteh pee-keh.*	**Me ha picado algo.** *Meh a pee-ka-doh al-goh.*	**Sono stato(a) punto(a).** *'Soh-noh 'sta-toh/ta 'poon-toh/ta.*	**Mich hat etwas gestochen.** *Mikh hat et-vass ge(r)-shtokhen.*
I feel dizzy.	**J'ai la tête qui tourne.** *Jeh la tet kee toorn.*	**Estoy mareado(a).** *Ehs-toh-ee ma-reh-a-doh/da.*	**Ho le vertigini.** *Oh leh vehr-'tee-jee-nee.*	**Mir ist schwindlig.** *Meer isst shwind-likh.*
It hurts here.	**J'ai mal ici.** *Jeh mal ee-see.*	**Me duele aquí.** *Meh dweh-leh a-kee.*	**Mi fa male qui.** *Mee fa 'ma-leh kwee.*	**Es tut hier weh.** *Ess toot heer vay.*
I'm constipated.	**Je suis constipé(-e).** *Je(r) swee ko(n)-stee-peh.*	**Tengo estreñimiento.** *Ten-goh ehs-treh-nyee-myehn-toh.*	**Sono stitico(a).** *'Soh-noh 'stee-tee-koh/ka.*	**Ich leide an Verstopfung.** *Ikh ly-de(r) an fer-shtopfoong.*
I'm allergic to . . .	**Je suis allergique à . . .** *Je(r) swee alair-jeek a . . .*	**Soy alérgico(a) a . . .** *Soh-ee a-lehr-ghee-koh/ka a . . .*	**Sono allergico(a) a . . .** *'Soh-noh al-'lehr-jee-koh/ka a . . .*	**Ich bin allergisch gegen . . .** *Ikh bin a-lair-gish gay-gen . . .*
I'm on the pill.	**Je prends la pilule.** *Je(r) pro(n) la peelew-l.*	**Estoy tomando anticonceptivos.** *Ehs-toh-ee toh-man-doh an-tee-kohn-thehp-tee-bohs.*	**Prendo la pillola.** *'Pren-doh la 'peel-loh-la.*	**Ich nehme die Pille.** *Ikh nay-me(r) dee pille(r).*

[1] Say this when you've been bitten by an animal.

Emergencies

	F
Help!	**Au secours!** *O se(r)-koor!*
Where's the police station?	**Où se trouve le commissariat de police?** *Oo se(r) troov le(r) komeesa-rya de(r) pol-eess?*
Please call...	**S'il vous plaît, appelez...** *Seel-voo-pleh, a-pleh...*
...the fire department	**les pompiers** *leh po(m)-pyeh*
...an ambulance	**une ambulance** *ewn o(m)-bew-lo(n)ss*
...the police	**la police** *la pol-eess*
I've been attacked.	**J'ai été attaqué(e).** *Jeh eteh atak-eh.*
I want to see a woman police officer.	**Je voudrais voir un officier de police femme.** *Je(r) voo-dreh vwa(r) un offee-syeh de(r) pol-eess fam.*
I've missed my plane.	**J'ai raté mon avion.** *Jeh rat-eh mon avyo(n).*

Missing objects

	F	S	I	G
I've lost...	**J'ai perdu...** *Jeh pair-dew...*	**He perdido...** *Eh pehr-dee-doh...*	**Ho perso...** *Oh 'pehr-soh...*	**Ich habe... verloren.** *Ikh hah-be(r)... fer-loren.*
Someone's stolen...	**On a volé...** *O(n) a vol-eh...*	**Alguien ha robado...** *Al-gyehn a roh-ba-doh...*	**Mi hanno rubato...** *Mee 'an-noh roo-'ba-toh...*	**Jemand hat... gestohlen.** *Yay-mant hat... ge(r)-shtoe-len.*
...my wallet	**mon porte-feuille** *mo(n) port-e(r)-fe(r)-ye(r)*	**mi billetera** *mee bee-lyeh-teh-ra*	**il portafoglio** *eel por-ta-'fol-lyo*	**meine Brieftasche** *mine(r) breef-tashe(r)*
...all my money	**tout mon argent** *too mo-nar-jo(n)*	**todo mi dinero** *toh-doh mee dee-neh-roh*	**tutti i soldi** *'toot-tee ee 'sol-dee*	**mein ganzes Geld** *mine gan-tsess gelt*
...my passport	**mon passeport** *mo(n) pass-po(r)*	**mi pasaporte** *mee pa-sa-pohr-teh*	**il passaporto** *eel 'pas-sa-'por-to*	**meinen Paß** *minen pass*
...my credit cards	**mes cartes de crédit** *meh kart de(r) kreh-dee*	**mis tarjetas de crédito** *mees tar-gheh-tas deh kreh-dee-toh*	**le carte di credito** *leh 'kar-teh dee 'kreh-dee-toh*	**meine Kreditkarten** *mine(r) kredeet-karten*

S	I	G
¡Ayuda! *¡A-yoo-da!*	**Aiuto!** *A-'yoo-toh!*	**Hilfe!** *Hil-fe(r)!*
¿Dónde está la comisaría (de policía)? *¿Dohn-deh ehs-ta la koh-mee-sa-ree-a (deh poh-lee-thee-a)?*	**Dove si trova il posto di polizia?** *'Doh-veh see 'troh-va eel 'pos-toh dee poh-lee-'tsee-a?*	**Wo ist die Polizeiwache?** *Voe isst dee poli-tsy-vakhe(r)?*
Por favor, llame a . . . *Pohr fa-bohr, lya-meh a . . .*	**Per favore, chiami . . .** *Pehr fa-'voh-reh 'kya-mee . . .*	**Bitte rufen Sie . . .** *Bitte(r) roofen zee . . .*
los bomberos *lohs bohm-beh-rohs*	**i vigili del fuoco** *ee 'vee-jee-lee del 'fwoh-koh*	**die Feuerwehr** *dee foyer-vair*
una ambulancia *oo-na am-boo-lan-thya*	**un'ambulanza** *oon am-boo-'lan-tsa*	**einen Krankenwagen** *eynen kranken-vah-gen*
la policía *la poh-lee-thee-a*	**la polizia** *la poh-lee-'tsee-a*	**die Polizei** *dee poli-tsy*
Me han asaltado. *Meh an a-sal-ta-doh.*	**Mi hanno picchiato(a).** *Mee 'an-noh 'peek-kya-toh/ta.*	**Ich wurde angegriffen.** *Ikh woorde(r) an-ge(r)-griffen.*
Quiero ver a una mujer policía. *Kyeh-roh behr a oo-na moo-ghehr poh-lee-thee-a.*	**Vorrei parlare con una poliziotta.** *Vor-'ray par-'la-reh kon oona poh-lee-'tsyot-ta.*	**Ich möchte eine Polizistin sprechen.** *Ikh mu(r)khte(r) eyne(r) poli-tsistin shprekhen.*
He perdido el avión. *Eh pehr-dee-doh ehl a-byon.*	**Ho perso l'aereo.** *O 'pehr-soh la-'eh-reh-oh.*	**Ich habe mein Flugzeug verpaßt.** *Ikh hah-be(r) mine floog-tsoyg fer-passt.*

	F	S	I	G
. . . my camera	**mon appareil-photo** *mo-napa-ray-fo-to*	**mi cámara fotográfica** *mee ka-ma-ra foh-toh-gra-fee-ka*	**la macchina fotografica** *la 'mak-kee-na foh-toh-'gra-fee-ka*	**meinen Fotoapparat** *minen foto-apparaht*
. . . my watch	**ma montre** *ma mo(n)tr*	**mi reloj** *mee reh-loh-gh*	**l'orologio** *loh-roh-'loj-joh*	**meine Uhr** *mine(r) ooer*
. . . my backpack	**mon sac à dos** *mo(n) sa-ka-do*	**mi mochila** *mee moh-tchee-la*	**lo zaino** *loh 'tsa-ee-noh*	**meinen Rucksack** *minen rook-sak*
. . . my handbag	**mon sac à main** *mo(n) sa-ka-ma(n)*	**mi bolso** *mee bohl-soh*	**la borsetta** *la bor-'set-ta*	**meine Handtasche** *mine(r) han-tashe(r)*
. . . my suitcase	**ma valise** *ma va-leez*	**mi maleta** *mee ma-leh-ta*	**la valigia** *la va-'lee-ja*	**meinen Koffer** *minen koffer*
. . . my key	**ma clé** *ma kleh*	**mi llave** *mee lya-beh*	**la chiave** *la 'kya-veh*	**mein Schlüssel** *mine shlewssel*

Departure: by air and sea

Booking a ticket

	F
I want to book a ticket to...	**Je voudrais réserver un billet pour...** *Je(r) voo-dreh reh-zair-veh u(n) bee-yeh poor...*
I'd like to confirm my flight.	**Je voudrais confirmer mon vol.** *Je(r) voo-dreh ko(n)-feer-meh mo(n) vol.*
What time should I check in?	**A quelle heure je dois me présenter?** *A kellu(r) je(r) dwa me(r) preh-son-teh?*
Where do I check my bags in?	**Où est-ce que je fais enregistrer mes bagages?** *Oo-esske(r) je(r) feh o(n)-reh-jee-streh meh ba-gahj?*
Has it been delayed?	**Est-ce qu'il a pris du retard?** *Ess-kee-la pree dew re(r)-tar?*
I want to change/cancel my ticket.	**Je voudrais changer/ annuler mon billet.** *Je(r) voo-dreh sho(n)-jeh/a-new-leh mo(n) bee-yeh.*

Helpful words

	F	S	I	G
airport	**l'aéroport** *lair-o-por*	**el aeropuerto** *ehl a-eh-roh-pwehr-toh*	**l'aereoporto** *la-eh-reh-oh-'por-toh*	**der Flughafen** *derr floog-hahfen*
port	**le port** *le(r) por*	**el puerto** *ehl pwehr-toh*	**il porto** *eel 'por-toh*	**der Hafen** *derr hahfen*
aeroplane	**l'avion** *lav-yo(n)*	**el avión** *ehl a-byohn*	**l'aereo** *la-'eh-reh-oh*	**das Flugzeug** *dass floog-tsoyg*
ferry	**le ferry** *le(r) ferry*	**el barco** *ehl bar-koh*	**il traghetto** *eel tra-'get-toh*	**die Fähre** *dee fay-re(r)*
departure gate	**la porte de départ** *la port de(r) deh-par*	**la puerta de salida** *la pwehr-ta deh sa-lee-da*	**l'uscita** *loo-'shee-ta*	**der Ausgang** *derr owss-gang*
boarding pass	**la carte d'embarquement** *la kart do(m)-bark-mo(n)*	**la tarjeta de embarque** *la tar-gheh-ta deh ehm-bar-keh*	**la carta d'imbarco** *la 'kar-ta deem-'bar-koh*	**die Bordkarte** *dee bord-karte(r)*
passport	**le passeport** *le(r) pass-por*	**el pasaporte** *ehl pa-sa-pohr-teh*	**il passaporto** *eel 'pas-sa-'por-toh*	**der Paß** *derr pass*
visa	**le visa** *le(r) vee-za*	**el visado** *ehl bee-sa-doh*	**il visto** *eel 'vee-stoh*	**das Visum** *dass vee-zoom*

S	I	G
Quisiera reservar un billete para . . . *Kees-yeh-ra reh-sehr-bar oon bee-lyeh-teh pa-ra . . .*	**Vorrei prenotare un biglietto per . . .** *Vor-'ray preh-noh-'ta-reh oon beel-'lyet-toh pehr . . .*	**Ich möchte eine Fahrkarte nach . . . buchen.** *Ikh mu(r)khte(r) eyner fahr-karte(r) nakh . . . bookhen.*
Quisiera confirmar mi vuelo. *Kees-yeh-ra kohn-feer-mar mee bweh-loh.*	**Vorrei confermare il volo.** *Vor-'ray kon-fehr-'ma-reh eel 'voh-loh.*	**Kann ich meinen Flug bestätigen?** *Kan ikh minen floog be(r)-shtetigen?*
¿A qué hora debo presentarme? *¿A keh oh-ra deh-boh preh-sehn-tar-meh?*	**A che ora bisogna presentarsi al check in?** *A keh 'oh-ra bee-'zoh-nya preh-zen-tar-see al check-in?*	**Wann muß ich einchecken?** *Van mooss ikh eyn-sheken?*
¿Dónde tengo que facturar el equipaje? *¿Dohn-deh tehn-goh keh fak-too-rar ehl eh-kee-pa-gheh?*	**Dove si fa il check in?** *'Doh-veh see fa eel check-in?*	**Wo ist die Abfertigung?** *Voe isst dee ap-fertigoong?*
¿Se ha retrasado? *¿Seh a reh-tra-sa-doh?*	**É in ritardo?** *Eh een ree-'tar-doh?*	**Hat er/es Verspätung?** *Hat air/ess fer-shpaytoong?*
Quiero cambiar/cancelar mi billete. *Kyeh-roh kam-byar/kan-theh-lar mee bee-lyeh-teh.*	**Vorrei cambiare/annullare il biglietto.** *Vor-'ray kam-'bya-reh/an-nool-'la-reh eel beel-'lyet-toh.*	**Ich möchte meine Fahrkarte ändern/stornieren.** *Ikh mu(r)khte(r) mine(r) fahr-karte(r) endern/shtor-neeren.*

	F	S	I	G
flight number	**le numéro de vol** *le(r) new-mair-ro de(r) vol*	**el número de vuelo** *ehl noo-meh-roh deh bweh-loh*	**il numero del volo** *eel 'noo-meh-roh del 'voh-loh*	**die Flugnummer** *dee floog-noomer*
standby	**sans garantie** *so(n) gäro(n)-tee*	**lista de espera** *lees-ta deh ehs-peh-ra*	**lista d'attesa** *'lee-sta dat-'teh-sa*	**Standby** *standby*
no smoking	**non-fumeurs** *no(n)-few-mu(r)*	**no fumador** *noh foo-ma-dohr*	**la zona non fumatori** *la 'dzoh-na non foo-ma-'toh-ree*	**Nichtraucher** *nikht-rowkher*
hand luggage	**les bagages à main** *leh ba-gahj a ma(n)*	**el equipaje de mano** *ehl eh-kee-pa-gheh deh ma-noh*	**i bagagli a mano** *ee ba-'gal-lyee a 'ma-noh*	**das Handgepäck** *dass hand-ge(r)pek*
duty free shop	**boutique hors taxe** *boo-teek or tax*	**tienda libre de impuestos** *tyehn-da lee-breh deh eem-pwehs-tohs*	**negozio duty free** *neh-'goh-tsyoh duty free*	**Duty free shop** *Duty free shop*
customs	**la douane** *la doo-ahn*	**la aduana** *la a-dwa-na*	**la dogana** *la doh-'ga-na*	**der Zoll** *derr tsoll*

French pronunciation

To pronounce French well you need the help of a French speaker or language tapes, but these general points will help. Bear in mind that there are exceptions and regional variations.

Vowel sounds

a can either be short and sound like the "a" in "cat", or long as in "ah".
e, eu and *oe* sound like "ur" in "fur". (In the pronunciation guide, e(r) means that *e* sounds like an unemphasised "the".)
é sounds like "a" as in "late", but clipped.
è, ê and *ai* sound like "ai" as in "air".
i, ie sound like "ee" in "been".
o sounds like "o" in "soft".
ô, au and *eau* sound like "oe" in "toe".
u sounds like "ew" in "few". Round your lips to say "oo", then try to say "ee" as well.
oi sounds like "wa" in "wagon".
ou sounds like "oo" in "moon".

Nasal sounds

Nasal sounds do not exist in English. The *n* or *m* is like a vibration in the back of your throat and they are not pronounced unless followed by a vowel or an "h".

For example, *vin* is pronounced va(n), *brun* is pronounced bru(n) and *enfant* is pronounced o(n)fo(n).

Consonants

ch sounds like "sh" in "shoe".
c sounds like "c" in "cat", except before "i" and "e" or with a ç when it is like "s" in "sit".
qu sounds like "c" as in "cat".
g sounds like "g" as in "go", except before "i" and "e" when it becomes soft like the "j" sound in "measure".
j sounds like a soft "g", as in "measure".
gn is like the "nio" sound as in "onion".
h is rarely pronounced.
ll when it follows "i" and "eu" is like "y" in "yes".
ail is like "y" in "sky".
r is a roll at the back of your throat.
s is usually like "ss" in "hiss", but may be like "z" in "zoo".
Consonants on ends of words are silent unless followed by a vowel when they are usually pronounced.

The alphabet in French

Ah, Beh, C = seh, Deh, E = ur, eFf, G = jeh, aHsh, I = ee, Jee, Kah, eLl, eM, eN, Oh, Peh, Q = kew, aiR, eSs, Teh, U = ew, Veh, W = doo-ble(r)-veh, X = ikss, Y = ee-grek, Z = tsed.

How French works

Nouns

All French nouns are either masculine (m) or feminine (f).

For a few nouns the gender is obvious, e.g. *le garçon* (boy) is masculine and *la fille* (girl) is feminine. For most nouns the gender seems random, e.g. *le tronc* (trunk) is masculine and *la branche* (branch) is feminine. Some nouns can be either gender, e.g. *le/la touriste* (tourist m/f) and some have two forms, e.g. *l'étudiant/l'étudiante* (student m/f).

The article (the word for "the" or "a") shows the gender of the noun:
with masculine nouns, "the" is *le*, e.g. *le train* (the train) and "a" is *un*, e.g. *un train* (a train);
with feminine nouns, "the" is *la*, e.g. *la boîte* (the box) and "a" is *une*, e.g. *une boîte* (a box);
with nouns that begin with a vowel[1], "the" is always *l'*, e.g. *l'avion* (the plane) or *l'étoile* (the star). "A" is still *un* or *une*, e.g. *un avion* (a plane) or *une étoile* (a star).

Sometimes French uses an article where English doesn't, e.g. *J'aime le thé* (I like tea).

To help you get articles right, the book gives nouns with the article most likely to be useful in the context, and the Index makes genders clear by listing nouns with *le* or *la*, or adding (m) or (f) after those that begin with a vowel.

Don't worry if you muddle up *le* and *la*, you will still be understood. It is worth knowing the gender of nouns since other words, particularly adjectives, change to match them. If you're learning a noun, learn it with *le* or *la* – or *un* or *une* for nouns that begin with a vowel.
A useful tip is that many nouns ending in "e" are feminine.

Plurals

In the plural, the French for "the" is *les*, e.g. *les trains* (the trains).

In English "some" (the plural for "a") is often left out. In French *un* or *une* becomes *des* in the plural and is always used, e.g. *Il y a des types qui...* (There are blokes who...).

To make a noun plural, add "s", e.g. *deux trains* (two trains). For some nouns you add "x", e.g. *deux gâteaux* (two cakes).

[1] "The" is also *l'* with some nouns that begin with "h", e.g. *l'heure* (the hour), *l'homme* (the man), *l'horloge* (the clock).

De, du, de la, de l', des (any, some)

When talking about things like butter or water, English uses "any", "some" or no article, e.g. Is there any butter left? I want some butter. There's water in the jug.

French has a special article that is always used in these cases, *de* + "the", but *de* + *le* are contracted to *du* and *de* + *les* to *des* so you use:
du + (m) noun, e.g. *Tu veux du café?* (Would you like some coffee?);
de la + (f) noun, e.g. *Tu as de la musique punk?* (Do you have any punk music?);
de l' + nouns beginning with a vowel, e.g. *Tu veux de l'eau gazeuse?* (Do you want any fizzy water?);
des + plural nouns, e.g. *Tu veux des frites?* (Do you want some chips?).

In negative sentences simply use *de* + noun, or *d'* before a vowel, e.g. *Je ne veux pas de café/d'eau* (I don't want any coffee/water).

De (of)

In French "of" is *de*. It works in the same way as *de* meaning "any, some": with (m) nouns use *du*, e.g. *la couleur du mur* (the colour of the wall), and so on.

French uses "of" to show possession where English does not, e.g. *le pull de Paul* (Paul's jumper, literally "the jumper of Paul").

Au, à la, à l', aux (to, at)

The French for "to" and "at" is *à*. With *le* and *les*, *à* contracts to *au* and *aux* so you use:
au + (m) nouns, e.g. *Je vais au ciné* (I'm going to the cinema);
à la + (f) nouns, e.g. *Je suis à la gare* (I'm at the station);
à l' + nouns that begin with a vowel, e.g. *Je suis à l'aéroport* (I'm at the airport);
aux + plural nouns, e.g. *Je vais aux Etats-Unis* (I'm going to the States).

Ceci, cela, ça (this, that)

"This" is *ceci*, "that" is *cela*, but both are shortened to *ça* in everyday French, e.g. *Je voudrais ça* (I'd like this/that).

Celui-ci and *celle-ci* are the (m) and (f) forms for "this one" and *celui-là* and *celle-là* are the (m) and (f) forms for "that one".

Ce, cette, cet, ces (this, that)

Used as an adjective, "this" and "that" are:
ce + (m) nouns, e.g. *ce type* (this bloke);
cette + (f) nouns, e.g. *cette fille* (this girl);
cet + nouns beginning with a vowel, e.g. *cet idiot* (that idiot);
ces + plural nouns, e.g. *ces filles* (those girls).

Adjectives

In French, many adjectives agree with the noun they refer to – they change when used with a feminine or plural noun.

Many add an "e" on the end when used with a (f) noun. The "e" also changes the sound of the word as it means you pronounce the consonant, e.g. *vert* (green) with a silent "t" becomes *verte* with a voiced "t": *un pull vert* (a green jumper), *une porte verte* (a green door).

Most adjectives that end in a vowel add an extra "e" but sound the same, e.g. *bleu/bleue*. In this book, adjectives that change are given twice, (m) form followed by (f) form, e.g. *vert/verte* (green). Some adjectives don't change, e.g. any that end in "e" like *sympathique* (nice).

In the plural, most adjectives add an "s", e.g. *des pulls verts* (green jumpers), *des portes vertes* (green doors).

Most adjectives come after the noun but some common ones usually come before, e.g.

beautiful	*beau/belle*	young	*jeune*
good	*bon/bonne*	pretty	*joli/jolie*
nice, kind	*gentil/gentille*	long	*long/longue*
big, tall	*grand/grande*	bad	*mauvais/mauvaise*
fat, big	*gros/grosse*	small/short	*petit/petite*
		old	*vieux/vieille*

Making comparisons

To make a comparison, put the following words in front of the adjective:
plus (more, ...er), e.g. *plus important* (more important), *plus gros* (fatter);
moins (less), e.g. *moins gros* (less fat);
aussi (as), e.g. *aussi gros* (as fat);
le plus/la plus (the most, the ...est), e.g. *le plus important* (the most important).

plus ... que (more ... than, ...er ... than), e.g. *Il est plus grand que Joe* (He's taller than Joe);
moins que (less ... than), e.g. *Elle est moins grande que lui* (She's less tall than him);
aussi ... que (as ... as), e.g. *Il est aussi maigre qu'elle* (He's as thin as her).
Que (than) shortens to *qu'* in front of a vowel.

There are some exceptions, e.g. *bon/bonne* (good), *meilleur/meilleure* (better), *le meilleur/la meilleure* (the best); *mauvais/mauvaise* (bad), *pire* (worse), *le pire/la pire* (the worst).

My, your, his, her etc.

In French these words agree with the noun they relate to, e.g. *mon frère* (my brother), *ma soeur* (my sister), *mes parents* (my parents).

In front of	(m) noun	(f) noun	plural noun
my	*mon*	*ma*	*mes*
your	*ton*	*ta*	*tes*
his/her	*son*	*sa*	*ses*
our	*notre*	*notre*	*nos*
your	*votre*	*votre*	*vos*
their	*leur*	*leur*	*leurs*

Before a vowel or "h", use the (m) form, e.g. *mon écharpe* (my scarf) even though *écharpe* is (f).

I, you, he, she etc.

I	*je* or *j'*	*Je* shortens to *j'* in front of vowels, e.g. *j'aime* (I like).
you	*tu* or *vous*	Say *tu* to a friend or someone your own age or younger. Use *vous* when you talk to someone older, whether you know them or not. If in doubt, use *vous*. Saying *tu* to someone who doesn't expect it can be rude. *Vous* is also the plural form. Use it when speaking to more than one person.
he	*il*	
she	*elle*	
it	*il* or *elle*	There is no special word for "it". Since nouns are (m) or (f), you use "he" to refer to a male or (m) thing and "she" to refer to a female or (f) thing, e.g. *Le train? Il est en retard* (The train? It's late.) or *La gare? Elle est là-bas* (The station? It's over there).
we	*nous* or *on*	*Nous* means "we", e.g. *Nous sommes en retard* (We are late). People often use *on* instead as *nous* sounds formal. Like "one" in English, *on* takes the he/she form of the verb: *On est en retard* (We're late, literally "One is late").
they	*ils* or *elles*	*Ils* is used for males and (m) things, and *elles* for females and (f) things.

Me, you, him etc.

me	*me*	him/it	*le*	us	*nous*
you	*te*	her/it	*la*	you	*vous*
				them	*les*

In French these come before the verb, e.g. *Je le veux* (I want it).

Verbs

French verbs have more tenses (present, future etc.) than English verbs, but there are simple ways of getting by which are explained here.

Present tense

Many French verbs end in "er" in the infinitive[1], e.g. *regarder* (to watch) and follow the same pattern. Drop "er" and replace it with the ending you need:

I watch	*je*	*regard e*
you watch	*tu*	*regard es*
he/she/it watches	*il/elle*	*regard e*
we watch	*nous*	*regard ons*
you watch	*vous*	*regard ez*
they watch	*ils/elles*	*regard ent*

French doesn't distinguish between the two English present tenses, e.g. I watch or I'm watching, so *je regarde* can mean either. Another tip is that verbs are easier than they look: many forms sound the same even though the spelling changes, e.g. *aime, aimes* and *aiment* all sound the same.

Useful irregular verbs

to be	*être*	to have (got)	*avoir*
I am	*je suis*		
you are	*tu es*	I have	*j'ai*
he/it is	*il est*	you have	*tu as*
she/it is	*elle est*	he/it has	*il a*
we are	*nous sommes*	she/it has	*elle a*
		we have	*nous avons*
you are	*vous êtes*	you have	*vous avez*
they are	*ils sont* *elles sont*	they have	*ils ont* *elles ont*

to want to	*vouloir*	to be able to	*pouvoir*
I want	*je veux*	I can	*je peux*
you want	*tu veux*	you can	*tu peux*
he/it wants	*il veut*	he/it can	*il peut*
she/it wants	*elle veut*	she/it can	*elle peut*
we want	*nous voulons*	we can	*nous pouvons*
you want	*vous voulez*	you can	*vous pouvez*
they want	*ils/elles veulent*	they can	*ils elles peuvent*

to have to/must	*devoir*
I have to/must	*je dois*
you have to/must	*tu dois*
he/it has to/must	*il doit*
she/it has to/must	*elle doit*
we have to/must	*nous devons*
you have to/must	*vous devez*
they have to/must	*ils/elles doivent*

[1]The infinitive, e.g. "to read", "to like" is the form in which verbs are given in the Index and in dictionaries. Many French infinitives end in "er", and quite a few end in "ir".

The last three verbs are handy for making sentences like:

Je veux manger (I want to eat);
Je peux venir avec toi (I can come with you);
Je dois regarder la télé (I must watch TV).

The second verb is in the infinitive[1]. The Index lists verbs in this form, and many French infinitives can be spotted by their "er" or "ir" endings.

to go	*aller*	to come	*venir*
I go	*je vais*	I come	*je viens*
you go	*tu vas*	you come	*tu viens*
he/it goes	*il va*	he/it comes	*il vient*
she/it goes	*elle va*	she/it comes	*elle vient*
we go	*nous allons*	we come	*nous venons*
you go	*vous allez*	you come	*vous venez*
they go	*ils vont elles vont*	they come	*ils/elles viennent*

Talking about the future

There is a future tense in French, e.g. *Je regarderai la télé* (I shall watch TV) but it is easier to use the "going to" future. *Je vais regarder la télé* (I'm going to watch the TV). For everyday use, this form is also more common. As in English, simply use the present of *aller* (to go) + an infinitive[1].

Talking about the past

The easiest way is to use the perfect tense, e.g. *j'ai regardé* which can mean "I watched" or "I have watched". You make the perfect with the present of *avoir* (to have) + the verb's past participle:
"er" verbs[1] change their ending to "é" in the past participle, e.g. *regarder* becomes *regardé* (they sound just the same);
"ir"[1] verbs change to "i", e.g. *dormir* becomes *dormi: il a dormi* (he slept/has slept).

Some verbs form the perfect tense with *être* (to be), e.g. *Il est allé* (he went/has been). Below are the most useful ones (past participles are also shown if they are not "er" or "ir" verbs):

to go	*aller*	to go home	*rentrer*
to arrive	*arriver*	to go back	*retourner*
to go down	*descendre, descendu*	to stay	*rester*
to become	*devenir, devenu*	to go out	*sortir*
to go in	*entrer*	to fall	*tomber*
to go up	*monter*	to come	*venir, venu*
to leave	*partir*		

The imperfect, or past, tense of "to be" and "to have" is also useful for talking about the past:

I was	*j'étais*	I had	*j'avais*
you were	*tu étais*	you had	*tu avais*
he/it was	*il était*	he/it had	*il avait*
she/it was	*elle était*	she/it had	*elle avait*
we were	*nous étions*	we had	*nous avions*
you were	*vous étiez*	you had	*vous aviez*
they were	*ils/elles étaient*	they had	*ils/elles avaient*

Negatives

To make a sentence negative, put *ne* and *pas* on either side of the verb, e.g. *je veux* (I want), *je ne veux pas* (I don't want) or *j'aime danser* (I like dancing), *je n'aime pas danser* (I don't like dancing).

In everyday, spoken French it is very common to drop the *ne*, e.g. *je veux pas* (I don't want).

Other useful negative words:
ne . . . jamais (never), e.g. *Il ne veut jamais* (He never wants);
ne . . . personne (nobody), e.g. *Je n'aime personne* (I don't like anybody);
ne . . . rien (nothing), e.g. *Je ne veux rien* (I don't want anything).

Making questions

The simplest way to make a question is to give a sentence the intonation of a question – raise your voice at the end, e.g. *il aime Anne* (He likes Anne) becomes *Il aime Anne?* (Does he like Anne?). This is everyday, spoken French.

Another way is to put *Est-ce que . . .?* at the beginning of the sentence, e.g. *Est-ce qu'il aime Anne?* (Does he like Anne?).

In more formal, polite French, you change the order of the words, e.g. *Voulez-vous du café?* (Would you like some coffee?) "T" goes between the verb and its subject if two vowels clash, e.g. *Aime-t-il Anne?* (Does he like Anne?).

As in English, many questions are formed using a special word like *pourquoi* (why?). The question is made in one of the three usual ways:
with no change to the sentence: *Pourquoi tu veux ça?* (Why do you want that?);
with *est-ce que: Pourquoi est-ce que tu veux ça?;*
with a change of order: *Pourquoi veux-tu ça?*

These words can be used in the same ways:

who?	*qui?*	where?	*où?*
what?	*quoi?*	how much?	*combien?*
when?	*quand?*	which?	*quel?*
how?	*comment?*	what?	

Spanish pronunciation

To pronounce Spanish well you need the help of a Spanish speaker or language tapes, but these general points will help. Bear in mind that there are exceptions and strong regional differences.

Vowels

a sounds like "a" in "cat".
e sounds like "e" in "let".
i sounds like "i" in "machine" except before "e" and "on" as in *ie* and *ión* when it sounds like "y" in "yawn".
o sounds like "o" in "pot".
u sounds like "oo" in "moon" except before "e" and "y" as in *ue* and *uy* when it sounds like "weh" and "wee". It is silent after "q" and "g".

Consonants

c is hard like "c" in "cat" except before "e" and "i" as in *ce* and *ci* when it sounds like "th" in "thumb". When it is before "h" as in *ch* it sounds like "ch" in "chocolate".
d sounds like the English "d" except at the end of a word when it is silent or like "th" in "that".
g sounds like "g" in "good" except before "e" and "i" as in *ge* and *gi* when it sounds like "ch" in the Scottish word "loch".
h is always silent.
j sounds like the "ch" in the Scottish "loch".
ll sounds like "l" followed by "y" as in "yes".
ñ sounds like "ni" in "onion".
qu sounds like the hard "c".
r is a rolled "r" especially at the beginning of a word.
v sounds like "b" in "big". There is no difference between a Spanish *v* and a Spanish *b*.
y sounds like the Spanish *i* at the end of a word or on its own as in *y*. In the middle of a word it sounds like "y" in "yes".

In Spanish you stress the final syllable of most words ending in a consonant. For words ending in a vowel, stress the second-to-last syllable. The stress mark (´ over a vowel) as in *día* is used when the general rule does not apply to show which syllable to stress.

The alphabet in Spanish

Applying the points made above, this is how you say the alphabet: *A, Be, Ce, CHe, De, E, eFe, Ge, Hache, I, Jota, Ka, eLe, eLLe, eMe, eÑe, O, Pe, Qu, eRe, eSe, Te, U, uVe, W = uVe doble, X = equis, Y = i griega, Z = ceta.*

How Spanish works

Nouns

All Spanish nouns are either masculine (m) or feminine (f). Nouns for people and animals have the obvious gender, e.g. *el padre* (father) and *el toro* (bull) are masculine and *la madre* (mother) and *la vaca* (cow) are feminine. For most nouns, though, the gender seems random, e.g. *autobús* (bus) is masculine and *casa* (house) is feminine. A few nouns can be either gender, e.g. *el/la turista* (tourist m/f).

The singular article (the word for "the" or "a") shows the noun's gender:
with (m) nouns, "the" is *el*, e.g. *el autobús* (the bus) and "a" is *un*, e.g. *un autobús* (a bus);
with (f) nouns, "the" is *la*, e.g. *la casa* (the house) and "a" is *una*, e.g. *una casa* (a house).

Don't worry if you muddle up *el* and *la*, you will still be understood. It is worth knowing the gender of nouns since other words, particularly adjectives, change to match them. If you're learning a noun, learn it with *el* or *la*. A useful tip is that many nouns ending in "a" are feminine.

Plurals

In the plural, the Spanish for "the" is *los* + masculine noun and *las* + feminine noun, e.g. *los autobuses* (the buses), *las casas* (the houses).
Uno and *una* become *unos* and *unas*, e.g. *unos autobuses* (some buses), *unas casas* (some houses).
To make nouns plural, add "es" to any that end in a consonant, e.g. *un tren, dos trenes* (a train, two trains) and add "s" to most nouns ending in a vowel, e.g. *un billete, dos billetes* (a ticket, two tickets).

A (to) and de (of, from)

In Spanish, "to" is *a*. When *a* precedes *el*, they contract to *al*, e.g. *Voy al mercado* (I'm going to the market).
The Spanish for "of" and "from" is *de*. When *de* precedes *el*, they join up and become *del*, e.g. *Soy del norte* (I'm from the north).
Spanish uses *de* to show possession where English does not, e.g. *el libro de Ana* (Ana's book), *el suéter del niño* (the kid's jumper).

Adjectives

In Spanish most adjectives come after the noun they refer to, e.g. *la película larga* (the long film). They also agree with the noun – they change when used with a feminine or plural noun.

With feminine nouns, adjectives ending in "o" and a few others change to "a", e.g. *corto* becomes *corta: la novela corta* (the short novel). Others don't change, e.g. *feliz* (happy). In this book adjectives that change are given twice with the (m) form first, e.g. *corto/corta* (short).

With plural nouns, most adjectives that end in a vowel have an "s", e.g. *rojo* (m) becomes *rojos: los trenes rojos* (the red trains); *roja* (f) becomes *rojas: las camisetas rojas* (the red T-shirts). Those that end in a consonant have "es", e.g. *difícil* (difficult) becomes *difíciles: los exámenes difíciles* (the difficult exams).

Some common adjectives come before the noun, e.g. *gran* (big), *poco/poca* (little).

Making comparisons

To make a comparison, put the following words in front of the adjective:
más (more,... er), e.g. *más bonita* (prettier);
menos (less), e.g. *menos bonita* (less pretty);
tan (as), e.g. *tan bonita* (as pretty);
el/la más (the most, the ...est), e.g. *la más bonita* (the prettiest);

más... que (more... than,... er... than), e.g. *El es más alto que ella* (He's taller than her);
menos que (less... than), e.g. *Ella es menos alta que él* (She's less tall than him);
tan... como (as... as), e.g. *El es tan delgado como ella* (He's as thin as her).

There are exceptions, e.g. *bueno/buena* (good), *mejor* (better), *el/la mejor* (the best); *malo/mala* (bad), *peor* (worse), *el/la peor* (the worst).

Very + adjective

Spanish has two ways of saying that something is "very good/easy etc.". You can use *muy* (very) + the adjective, e.g. *muy fácil* (very easy), or the adjective + *-ísimo/ísima*, e.g. *facilísimo/facilísima* (very easy). Vowels on the end of the adjective are dropped, e.g. *caro* (expensive), *carísimo* (very expensive). This second way is used a lot in colloquial Spanish.

Este/esta (this)

The Spanish for "this" is *este* + (m) noun, e.g. *este chico* (this boy), *esta* + (f), e.g. *esta chica* (this girl), *estos* + plural (m) noun, e.g. *estos chicos* (these boys), *estas* + plural (f), e.g. *estas chicas* (these girls).

Ese/esa, aquel/aquella (that)

There are two words for "that": *ese* when the person or thing referred to is near the person you're speaking to, e.g. who's that bloke on your right?, and *aquel* when the person or thing is far from both of you, e.g. that bloke over there.
Ese and *aquel* change as follows: *ese* or *aquel* + (m) noun; *esa* or *aquella* + (f); *esos* or *aquellos* + plural (m) noun; *esas* or *aquellas* + plural (f).

I, you, he, she etc.

Spanish often leaves out "I", "you" etc. The verb changes according to who or what is doing the action (see Verbs, page 68) so they are not needed, e.g. *Estoy pensando* (I am thinking, literally "am thinking"), *Es un bar* (It's a bar, literally "Is a bar"). It helps to know these words as the verb has various forms to correspond to each of them.

I *yo*	
you *tú* or *usted*	There are four words for "you": *tú* is singular informal; say *tú* to a friend or someone your age or younger; *usted*, often written *Vd.*, is singular polite (pol). Use it to a person you don't know or you want to show respect to (someone older);
vosotros/vosotros or *ustedes*	*vosotros/-as* is plural informal, (m)/(f). Use it like *tú* but when speaking to more than one person. Use *vosotras* when talking to girls or women only; *ustedes* (written *Vds.*) is plural polite (pl.pol.). Use it like *usted* but for more than one person. If in doubt, use the polite forms. Saying *tú* or *vosotros* to people who don't expect it can be rude.
he *él*	
she *ella*	
it *(él/ella)*	There's no special word for "it". The verb is used on its own.
we *nosotros/nosotras*	*Nosotros* means "we" for males or males and females, *nosotras* means "we" for females only.
they *ellos* or *ellas*	*Ellos* is for males, *ellas* for females.

My, your, his, her etc.

These words agree with the noun they relate to, e.g. *mi hermano* (my brother), *mis padres* (my parents), *nuestra casa* (our house) etc.:

	in front of singular noun	plural noun
my	*mi*	*mis*
your	*tu*	*tus*
his/her/its your (pol)	*su*	*sus*
our	*nuestro/nuestra*	*nuestros/nuestras*
your	*vuestro/vuestra*	*vuestros/vuestras*
their, your (pl.pol)	*su*	*sus*

Verbs

Spanish verbs have more tenses – present, future, simple past etc. – than English verbs, but there are simple ways of getting by which are explained here.

Present tense

Spanish verbs end in "ar", "er" or "ir" in the infinitive[1], e.g. *comprar* (to buy), *comer* (to eat), *escribir* (to write), and follow one of these three patterns. Drop "ar", "er" or "ir" and replace it with the ending you need:

to buy *compr ar*

I buy	*compr o*	we buy	*compr amos*
you buy	*compr as*	you buy	*compr áis*
he/she/it buys, you (pol) buy	*compr a*	they/you (pl.pol) buy	*compr an*

to eat *com er*

I eat	*com o*	we eat	*com emos*
you eat	*com es*	you eat	*com éis*
he/she/it eats, you (pol) eat	*com e*	they/you (pl.pol) eat	*com en*

to write *escrib ir*

I write	*escrib o*	we write	*escrib imos*
you write	*escrib es*	you write	*escrib ís*
he/she/it writes, you (pol) write	*escrib e*	they/you (pl.pol) write	*escrib en*

Spanish verbs are mostly used without "I", "you" etc. (see I, you, he, she etc. on page 67). It helps to learn them as a list, e.g. *como, comes* etc.

Spanish doesn't distinguish as much as English between present (I write) and present continuous (I'm writing). Unless you want to stress that the action is happening now (e.g. He's sleeping), the present tense is used, e.g. *Viene hoy* (she is coming today, literally "She comes today").

Ser and estar (to be)

Spanish has two verbs "to be". *Ser* is used to describe people and things, e.g. *Soy ingles* (I am English), *Es un camarero* (He's a waiter), and to tell the time, e.g. *Son las tres* (It's three). *Estar* is for saying where people and things are, e.g. *Está lejos* (It's far) and describing anything changeable or short-lived, e.g. *Está de mal humor* (He's in a bad mood). Both are irregular:

to be	*ser*	*estar*
I am	*soy*	*estoy*
you are	*eres*	*estás*
he/she/it is you (pol) are	*es*	*está*
we are	*somos*	*estamos*
you are	*sois*	*estáis*
they/you (pl.pol) are	*son*	*están*

Other useful irregular verbs

to have (got)	*tener*
I have (got)	*tengo*
you have (got)	*tienes*
he/she/it has (got) you (pol) have (got)	*tiene*
we have (got)	*tenemos*
you have (got)	*tenéis*
they have (got) you (pl.pol) have (got)	*tienen*

	to do	*hacer*	to go	*ir*
I	do	*hago*	go	*voy*
you	do	*haces*	go	*vas*
he/she/it	does	*hace*	goes	*va*
you (pol)	do		go	
we	do	*hacemos*	go	*vamos*
you	do	*hacéis*	go	*vais*
they	do	*hacen*	go	*van*
you (pl.pol)	do		go	

to be able to (can) *poder*

I can	*puedo*	we can	*podemos*
you can	*puedes*	you can	*podéis*
he/she/it you (pol) can	*puede*	they/you (pl.pol) can	*pueden*

Stem-changing verbs

These are verbs whose stem (the part before the infinitive[1] ending) changes as well as the endings. These three are especially useful:

to want *querer*

I want	*quiero*	we want	*queremos*
you want	*quieres*	you want	*queréis*
he/she/it wants, you (pol) want	*quiere*	they/you (pl.pol) want	*quieren*

[1] The infinitive is the form in which verbs are given in the Index and in dictionaries. Many Spanish infinitives end in "ar", "er" or "ir". Reflexive verbs end in "se".

to prefer	*preferir*		
I prefer	*prefiero*	we prefer	*preferimos*
you prefer	*prefieres*	you prefer	*preferís*
he/she/it you (pol) prefer(s)	*prefiere*	they/you (pl.pol) prefer	*prefieren*

to play	*jugar*		
I play	*juego*	we play	*jugamos*
you play	*juegas*	you play	*jugáis*
he/she/it plays, you (pol) play	*juega*	they/you (pl.pol) play	*juegan*

Reflexive verbs

Spanish has far more reflexive verbs than English. They all have "se" infinitive[1] endings, e.g. *lavarse* (to get washed/wash oneself), *levantarse* (to get up, literally "to get oneself up"). Here is the present of a common one:

I get up	*me levanto*
you get up	*te levantas*
he/she/you (pol) gets up	*se levanta*
we get up	*nos levantamos*
you get up	*os levantáis*
they/you (pl.pol) get up	*se levantan*

Talking about the future

"Ar", "er" and "ir" verbs (see Present tense) all have the same endings in the future tense:

I shall buy	*comprar é*
you will buy	*comprar ás*
he/she/it will buy you (pol) will buy	*comprar á*
we shall buy	*comprar emos*
you will buy	*comprar éis*
they/you (pl.pol) will buy	*comprar án*

Another future tense is made with the present of *ir* (to go) + *a* + the verb's infinitive, e.g. *Voy a comprar* (I'm going to buy). It is used for something that is just about to happen.

Talking about the past

The most useful past tense in Spanish is the simple past tense. "Ar" verbs have one set of endings and "er" and "ir" verbs have another:

to buy	*compr ar*		
I bought	*compr é*	we bought	*compr amos*
you bought	*compr aste*	you bought	*compr asteis*
he/she/it you (pol) bought	*compr ó*	they/you (pl.pol) bought	*compr aron*

to eat	*com er*		
I ate	*com í*	we ate	*com imos*
you ate	*com iste*	you ate	*com isteis*
he/she/it you (pol) ate	*com io*	they/you (pl.pol) ate	*com ieron*

The past tenses of "to be" and "to do" are also useful:

to be	*ser*	*estar*
I was	*fui*	*estuve*
you were	*fuiste*	*estuviste*
he/she/it was you (pol) were	*fue*	*estuvo*
we were	*fuimos*	*estuvimos*
you were	*fuisteis*	*estuvisteis*
they/you (pl.pol) were	*fueron*	*estuvieron*

The past tense of *ir* (to go) is the same as the past tense of *ser*, so *fui* can also mean "I went", *fue* (he/she/it went), *fuimos* (we went) etc.

to do	*hacer*		
I did	*hice*	we did	*hicimos*
you did	*hiciste*	you did	*hicisteis*
he/she/it you (pol) did	*hizo*	they/you (pl.pol) did	*hicieron*

Negatives

To make a sentence negative put *no* in front of the verb, e.g. *No comprendo* (I don't understand), *No me levanto* (I don't get up).

Other useful negative words include *nunca* (never), *nadie* (nobody), *nada* (nothing), *ninguno/ninguna* (any).

Making questions

To make a question, just give a sentence the intonation of a question – raise your voice at the end. In written Spanish you put an upside down question mark at the start and a standard one at the end, e.g. *¿Quieres comer?* (Do you want to eat?).

Questions can begin with words like:

who?	*¿quién?*
what?	*¿qué?*
when?	*¿cuándo?*
how?	*¿cómo?*
where?	*¿dónde?*
how much?	*¿cuánto/cuánta?*
which? what?	*¿cuál?*

Exclamations

In written Spanish you put an upside down exclamation mark at the start and a standard one at the end, e.g. *¡Claro!* (Of course!)

Italian pronunciation

To pronounce Italian well you need the help of an Italian speaker or language tapes, but these general points will help. Bear in mind that there are exceptions and regional variations.

Vowels

a sounds like the "a" in "apple".
e sounds like the "e" in "ten".
i sounds like the "ee" in "see".
o sounds like the "o" in "hot".
u is like the "oo" in "boot".

Consonants

c before "e" or "i" sounds like "ch".
g before "e" or "i" sounds like "j".
c before "a", "o", "u" sounds like "k".
g before "a", "o", "u" sounds like "g".
ch sounds like "k".
gh sounds like "g".
gli sounds like "lli" in "brilliant".
gn sounds like "ni" in "onion".
h is silent.
r is rolled.
s sounds like "s" or "z".
sc before "e" or "i" sounds like "sh".
sc before "a", "o", "u" sounds like "sk".
sch sounds like "sk".
z sounds like "ts" or "dz".
Where alternatives are given, it depends on the context. When a vowel sound is followed by a double consonant, it is shorter.

Stress

In many words the stress is on the last syllable but one. In the pronunciation guide in this book, stress is indicated by ' before the stressed syllable.

The alphabet in Italian

Applying the points above, this is how you say the alphabet: *A, Bi, Ci, Di, E = Eh, eFfe, Gi, H = 'ak-ka, I = ee, J = ee-'lun-ga, Kappa, eLle, eMme, eNne, O, Pi, Q = koo, eRre, eSse, Ti, U = oo, Vi, W = vi 'dop-pya, X = ics, Y = 'ip-si-lon, Z = 'dzeh-ta.*

How Italian works

Nouns

All Italian nouns are either masculine (m) or feminine (f). For some nouns the gender is obvious, e.g. *il padre* (father) is masculine and *la madre* (mother) is feminine. For most nouns though the gender seems random, e.g. *il tavolo* (table) is masculine and *la sedia* (chair) is feminine. Some nouns can be either gender, e.g. *il/la turista* (tourist m/f).

The article shows the gender of the noun: with singular (m) nouns, "the" is *il*, and "a" is *un*, except before nouns beginning with *s* + consonant or *z* (and some uncommon ones in *x, ps, pn and gn*) where "the" is *lo* and "a" is *uno*, e.g. *lo/uno studente* (the/a student), *lo/uno zoo* (the/a zoo);
with (f) nouns, "the" is *la* and "a" is *una*, except before nouns beginning with a vowel where "a" is *un'*, e.g. *un'amica* (a friend);
with nouns beginning with a vowel, whether masculine or feminine "the" is always *l'* e.g. *l'albergo* (the hotel) or *l'agenzia* (the agency).

To help you get the articles right, the book gives nouns with the article most likely to be useful in the context, and the Index makes genders clear by listing nouns preceded by the article or adding (m) or (f) after those that begin with a vowel. It's worth knowing the gender of nouns since other words change to match them.

Plurals

In the plural, the Italian for "the" is *i* + (m) nouns that take *il* in the singular, e.g. *i treni* (the trains) and *gli* + (m) nouns that take *lo* in the singular, e.g. *gli studenti* (the students). With plural feminine nouns, "the" is always *le*, e.g. *le ragazze* (the girls).

In the plural *un, uno* and *una* become *dei, degli* and *delle*, e.g. *dei treni* (some trains), *degli studenti* (some students) *delle case* (some houses).

To make nouns plural you have to change the ending vowel:

from *o* (m)	to *i*,	e.g. *il treno, i treni*
from *a* (f)	to *e*,	e.g. *la casa, le case*
from *e* (m/f)	to *i*,	e.g. *il fiore, i fiori*

Masculine nouns ending in *a* in the singular end in *i* in the plural, e.g. *un turista, due turisti* (a tourist, two tourists). Nouns ending in consonants or accented vowels do not change in the plural, e.g. *il bar, i bar* (the bar, the bars), *la città, le città* (the town, the towns). There are a few irregular plurals.

Di + "the" (some, any)

Italian has a special article that is used to express the idea of "some" or "any" with singular nouns, *di* + "the", *di* + *il* contracts to *del, di* + *lo* to *dello, di* + *la* to *della* and *di* +

l' to *dell'*, e.g. *Vorrei dell'acqua minerale* (I'd like some mineral water).

Di (of)

The Italian for "of" is *di*. When *di* precedes an article, they join up in the same way as *di* + "the" meaning "some, any", e.g. *il colore del tavolo* (the colour of the table) and so on. Italian uses "of" to show possession where English does not, e.g. *la giacca del ragazzo* (the boy's jacket).

A (to), da (from), in (in), su (on)

When these prepositions precede "the" they contract in the same way as *di* + "the", so a + il becomes al, in + la is nella and so on. E.g. *È nella stanza* (He's in the room).

Adjectives

In Italian most adjectives agree with the noun they refer to – they change when used with a feminine or plural noun.
Adjectives ending in "o" in the masculine, change to "a" in the feminine, to "i" in the (m) plural and to "e" in the (f) plural, e.g. *lungo* (long) becomes *lunga, lunghi, lunghe.*

Adjectives ending in "e" in the masculine do not change in the feminine and change to "i" in the plural whether (m) or (f), e.g. *felice* (m/f), *felici* (plural m/f), e.g. *un uomo felice* (a happy man), *una donna felice* (a happy woman).
A few adjectives do not change at all, e.g. *blu* (blue), *rosa* (pink).

In Italian most adjectives come after the noun they refer to, but some common ones can also precede the noun, e.g. *un caro amico* (a dear friend), *una bella giornata* (a beautiful day).

Very + adjective

Italian has two ways of saying that something is very good, easy, etc. You can use *molto* (very) + the adjective, e.g. *molto facile* (very easy) or the adjective + *-issimo/-issimi* (m) + *-issima/-issime* (f), e.g. *facilissimo/facilissimi, facilissima/facilissime* (very easy).
This second way is more emphatic and used a lot in colloquial Italian.

My, your, his, her etc.

In Italian these words agree with the noun they relate to, e.g. *mio fratello* (my brother), *mia sorella* (my sister), *I miei genitori* (my parents), *la nostra casa* (our house).

Italian often doesn't use "my", "your" etc. where English does e.g. *Ho perso il portafogli* (I lost my wallet, literally "I lost the wallet").

I, you, he, she etc.

Italian often leaves out "I", "you" etc. The verb changes according to who or what is doing the action (see Verbs) so they are not needed, e.g. *Stanno studiando* (They are studying, literally "Are studying"). However, it is worth knowing these words as they will be used to clarify, emphasise and contrast e.g. *Io lavoro e lui dorme* (I'm working and he's sleeping). Here are the words for "I, you, he" etc. with their appropriate uses.

I	*io*	
you	*tu*	The informal singular. Use it to a friend or someone your age or younger.
	lei	*lei* is the polite singular. Use it to a person you don't know or you want to show respect to (someone older). It takes the he/she form of the verb.
	voi	*voi* is the plural form. Use it when speaking to more than one person.
he	*lui*	
she	*lei*	
it		There is no special word for "it". The verb is used on its own, e.g. *É tardi* (It's late).
we	*noi*	
they	*loro*	

Me, you, him etc.

In Italian there are two different ways of saying me, you, him etc.

me	*me/mi*
you	*te/ti*
you (pol) her	*lei/le*
him	*lui/gli*
us	*noi/ci*
you	*voi/vi*
them	*loro/loro*

The first ones are used after prepositions and have more stress in the sentence, e.g. *Questo è per me* (This one is for me). The second ones come before the verb, e.g. *Mi può dire dov'è la stazione?* (Can you tell me where the station is?). With some verbs *mi, ti* etc. can be found either before the verb or joined onto the end of the verb, e.g. *Mi può dire/può dirmi?* (Can you tell me?). When it is added to the end of the verb the vowel at the end of the verb drops.

When "him", "her", "you" (pol) and "them" are used with a transitive verb (one that does not take a preposition) they become *lo* (him/it), *la* (her/it), *la* (you, pol.), *li/le* (them m/f), e.g. *La vedo spesso* (I see her often), *Li prendo, grazie* (I'll take them, thanks).

Verbs

Italian verbs have more tenses (present, future etc.) than English verbs, but there are simple ways of getting by which are explained here.

Present tense

Italian verbs end in "are", "ere" or "ire" in the infinitive1, e.g. *imparare* (to learn), *vendere* (to sell), *sentire* (to hear) and *capire* (to understand) and follow one of these patterns. Note that there are two "ire" patterns. Drop "are", "ere" or "ire" and replace it with the ending you need:

to learn	*imparare*
I learn	*impar o*
you learn	*impar i*
he/she/it learns, you (pol) learn	*impar a*
we learn	*impar iamo*
you learn	*impar ate*
they learn	*impar ano*

to hear	*sentire*
I hear	*sent o*
you hear	*sent i*
he/she/it hears, you (pol) hear	*sent e*
we hear	*sent iamo*
you hear	*sent ite*
they hear	*sent ono*

to sell	*vendere*
I sell	*vend o*
you sell	*vend i*
he/she/it sells, you (pol) sell	*vend e*
we sell	*vend iamo*
you sell	*vend ete*
they sell	*vend ono*

to understand	*capire*
I understand	*cap isco*
you understand	*cap isci*
he/she/it understands, you (pol) understand	*cap isce*
we understand	*cap iamo*
you understand	*cap ite*
they understand	*cap iscono*

Italian verbs are mostly used without "I", "you" etc. (see I, you, he, she etc.). It helps to learn verbs as a list, e.g. *imparo, impari* etc.

Italian doesn't distinguish as much as English between the present simple (I write) and the present continuous (I'm writing). Unless you want to stress the action is happening now you can use the present simple tense, e.g. *Viene oggi* (He's coming today, literally "He comes today").

Italian sometimes uses the present simple tense where English uses the future tense, e.g. *Prendo questo, grazie* (I'll take this one, thanks, literally "I take this one, thanks"), and also where English uses a past tense, e.g. *Studio italiano da tre mesi* (I've been studying Italian for three months, literally "I study Italian for three months").

Useful irregular verbs

to be	*essere*
I am	*sono*
you are	*sei*
he/she/it is, you (pol) are	*è*
we are	*siamo*
you are	*siete*
they are	*sono*
to do	*fare*
I do	*faccio*
you do	*fai*
he/she/it does, you (pol) do	*fa*
we do	*facciamo*
you do	*fate*
they do	*fanno*

to have to/must	*dovere*
I have to/must	*devo*
you have to/must	*devi*
he/she/it has to/must, you (pol) have to/must	*deve*
we have to/must	*dobbiamo*
you have to/must	*dovete*
they have to/must	*devono*

to be able to/can	*potere*
I can	*posso*
you can	*puoi*
he/she/it can, you (pol) can	*può*
we can	*possiamo*
you can	*potete*
they can	*possono*

to have	*avere*
I have	*ho*
you have	*hai*
he/she/it has, you (pol) have	*ha*
we have	*abbiamo*
you have	*avete*
they have	*hanno*
to want	*volere*
I want	*voglio*
you want	*vuoi*
he/she/it wants, you (pol) want	*vuole*
we want	*vogliamo*
you want	*volete*
they want	*vogliono*

The conditional

When asking for something, it is polite to use the conditional tense instead of the present, e.g. *Mi faresti un favore?* (Could you do me a favour?) and *Vorrei delle mele.* (I'd like some apples.). *Voglio delle mele.* (I want some apples) sounds bad mannered.
You will find the following expressions useful:
Vorrei... (I would like), *Vorremmo...* (We would like);
Potrei...? (May I ...?), *Potresti...?* (Could you...?) (sing. informal);
Potrebbe...? (Could you...?) (sing. pol.), *Potremmo...?* (Could we...?)

The imperative

When giving instructions and directions, Italian uses the imperative e.g. *Prenda la prima a destra.* (Take the first on the right). Only the *tu/lei* imperative forms are different from the present tense forms. With regular verbs, just drop the *"are"*, *"ere"*, *"ire"* infinitive endings and add the imperative endings. This is how you form imperatives from *arrivare* (to arrive), *prendere* (to take), and *seguire* (to follow):

tu (sing. informal)	*lei* (sing. pol.)
arriv-a	*arriv-i*
prend-i	*prend-a*
segu-i	*segu-a*

Talking about the future

There is a future tense in Italian, e.g. *Partirò domani* (I'm leaving tomorrow) but in everyday speech the present tense is often used to express the idea of future, e.g. *Parto tra un mese* (I'm leaving in a month's time, literally "I leave in a month's time"), *Ci vediamo dopo* (I'll see you later, literally "We see each other later").

Talking about the past

The most useful past tense in Italian is the perfect tense, e.g. *Ho comprato un libro* which can mean "I bought a book" or "I have bought a book". With most verbs you make the perfect with the present of *avere* (to have) + the verb's past participle. With regular verbs the endings change like this:

"are"	*ato*	e.g.	*mangiare, mangiato*
"ere"	*uto*	e.g.	*vendere, venduto*
"ire"	*ito*	e.g.	*capire, capito*

So the perfect will be *ho mangiato* (I ate/have eaten), *ho venduto* (I sold/have sold), *ho capito* (I understood/have understood).

Some verbs form the present perfect with *essere* (to be), e.g. *Sono andato* (I went/have gone). With verbs that take *essere* the past participle agrees with the subject in gender and number, e.g. *Sono andata* (I went/have been) if the "I" is female, *Siamo andati* (we went/have been), *Siamo andate*, if the "we" are all females. Nearly all the verbs that take *essere* are verbs of motion, e.g. *andare* (to go), *venire* (to come), *uscire* (to go out), etc.

Here is a list of useful irregular past participles used in the "I" form of the perfect tense:

essere (to be) *sono stato(a)* (I have been/was).
rimanere (to stay) *sono rimasto/rimasta* (I stayed/have stayed).
fare (to do) *ho fatto* (I did/have done).
dire (to say) *ho detto* (said/I have said).
chiedere (to ask) *ho chiesto* (I asked/have asked).
vedere (to see) *ho visto* (I saw/have seen).
chiudere (to close) *ho chiuso* (I closed/have closed).
aprire (to open) *ho aperto* (I opened/have opened).
rispondere (to answer) *ho risposto* (I answered/have answered).

Negatives

To make a sentence negative put "non" in front of the verb, e.g. *Non ho capito* (I didn't understand). If you are using *mi, ti* etc. remember that these words go between *non* and the verb, e.g. *Non mi ha visto* (he didn't see me), *Non lo so* (I don't know).

Questions

To make a question, just give a sentence the intonation of a question – raise your voice at the end, e.g. *É partita* (She's left), becomes *É partita?* (Has she left?)

German pronunciation

To pronounce German well you need the help of a German speaker or language tapes, but these general points will help. Bear in mind that there are exceptions and strong regional variations.

Vowel sounds

a can either be short and sound like the "a" in "cat" with a hint of the "u" in "cut", or long as in "ah".
ä sounds like "e" in "next".
au sounds like "ow" in "cow".
äu and *eu* sounds like "oy" in "boy".
e sounds like "e" in "get" and is always pronounced at the end of a word.
ei sounds like "i" in "mine" or "ey" in "eye".
i is sometimes short and said like "i" in "fish". When it is long it is the same as *ie* and *ih* and sounds like "ee" as in "been".
ö sounds like "u" in "surf".
u sounds like "oo" in "moon".
ü sounds like "ew" as in "few". Round your lips to say "oo", then try to say "ee" as well.

Consonant sounds

b sounds like "b" as in "bat", or at the end of a word it sounds nearly like "p".
ch sounds like "ch" in the Scottish word "loch".
d sounds like "d" as in "dog". On the end of a word it sounds like "t".
g sounds like "g" as in "got". On the end of a word it sounds like "ch" as in "loch".
h sounds like "h" as in "hat". After a vowel the *h* is silent making the vowel long.
j sounds like "y" as in "yes".
qu sounds like "k" plus "v".
r is rolled more towards the back of the throat than in English.
s sounds like "z" as in "zoo" before a vowel. Before consonants or at the end of a word, it sounds like "ss" in "hiss". When it is before "p" or "t", it sounds like "sh" in "short".
sch sounds like "sh" in "short".
ß is a German letter. It sounds like "ss" in "hiss".
v usually sounds like "f" as in "fine".
w sounds like "v" as in "very".
z sounds like "ts" in "hits".

The alphabet in German

Ah, Beh, C = tseh, Deh, Eh, efF, Geh, Ha, I = ee, J = yot, Kah, elL, emM, enN, Oh, Peh, Q = koo, aiR, esS, Teh, U = oo, V = fow, W = veh, X = iks, Y = ewpsilon, Z = tset.

How German works

Nouns

All German nouns are written with a capital first letter. They are either masculine (m), feminine (f) or neuter (n). For a few the gender is obvious, e.g. *Mann* (man) is (m) and *Frau* (woman) is (f), but for most animals and things, the gender seems random, e.g. *Zug* (train) is (m), *Fähre* (ferry) is (f), and *Auto* (car) is (n). Even with nouns for people you can't always guess the gender, e.g. *Mädchen* (girl) is (n). Some nouns have two forms, e.g. *der Lehrer/die Lehrerin* (teacher m/f).

The definite article (the word for "the") shows a noun's gender. With (m) nouns "the" is *der*, e.g. *der Zug* (the train). With (f) nouns "the" is *die*, e.g. *die Fähre* (the ferry). With (n) nouns "the" is *das*, e.g. *das Auto* (the car).

Don't worry if you muddle up *der, die* and *das*, you will still be understood. It is worth knowing genders of nouns since other words, particularly adjectives, change to match them, and the articles change in the different cases (see Cases). If you learn a noun, learn it with *der, die* or *das* (the Index lists nouns with *der, die* or *das*).

Plurals

In the plural, "the" is *die*, e.g. *die Züge* (the trains). Most noun endings change in the plural and some nouns also add an umlaut (¨) over a vowel. The Index gives plural noun endings. When you learn a noun, learn its plural as well, e.g. *der Zug, die Züge*.

Cases

German nouns have four cases, or forms, depending on the job they do in a sentence. The noun ending sometimes changes and the article often changes. The four cases are:
nominative – a noun is nominative when it is the subject of a sentence (the person or thing doing the action). In *Die Frau repariert das Rad* (the woman is repairing the bike), *die Frau* (the woman) is nominative;
accusative – a noun is accusative when it is the direct object (the person or thing that the action directly affects). In the example above, *das Rad* (the bike) is accusative;
genitive – a noun is genitive when it shows whose something is. In *Die Frau repariert das Rad des Mannes* (The woman is repairing the man's bike), *des Mannes* (the man's) is genitive;

dative – a noun is dative when it is the indirect object (the person or thing for whom something is being done). In *Die Frau gibt das Rad dem Mann* (The woman gives the bike to the man), *dem Mann* (the man) is dative.

Since *der, die* and *das* change with the four cases, it helps to learn them as a chart:

	(m)	(f)	(n)
singular:	the man	the woman	the child
nom	*der Mann*	*die Frau*	*das Kind*
acc	*den Mann*	*die Frau*	*das Kind*
gen	*des Mannes*	*der Frau*	*des Kindes*
dat	*dem Mann*	*der Frau*	*dem Kind*
plural:	the men	the women	the children
nom	*die Männer*	*die Frauen*	*die Kinder*
acc	*die Männer*	*die Frauen*	*die Kinder*
gen	*der Männer*	*der Frauen*	*der Kinder*
dat	*den Männern*	*den Frauen*	*den Kindern*

In everyday German the "e" in the genitive singular is dropped, e.g. *des Manns* (the man's).

Ein/eine/ein (a, an)

The indefinite article, (the word for "a") is *ein* with (m) and (n) nouns, and *eine* with (f) nouns. It also changes according to case:

	a man	a woman	a child
nom	*ein Mann*	*eine Frau*	*ein Kind*
acc	*einen Mann*	*eine Frau*	*ein Kind*
gen	*eines Mannes*	*einer Frau*	*eines Kindes*
dat	*einem Mann*	*einer Frau*	*einem Kind*

German has no plural indefinite article ("some" in English). The plural noun is used on its own, e.g. *Ich habe Äpfel* (I have apples).

Adjectives

In sentences like *Das Rad ist neu* (The bike is new), adjectives don't change. In front of a noun, e.g. *ein neues Rad* (a new bike), their ending changes to match the noun's case and gender. They change differently with "the" and "a":

Adjectives after *der/die/das* (the):

singular:	(m)	(f)	(n)
nom	*der neue Film*	*die neue Platte*	*das neue Buch*
acc	*den neuen Film*	*die neue Platte*	*das neue Buch*
gen	*des neuen Films*	*der neuen Platte*	*das neuen Buchs*
dat	*dem neuen Film*	*der neuen Platte*	*dem neuen Buch*

(plural (m)/(f)/(n):

nom	*die neuen Filme/Platten/Bücher*
acc	*die neuen Filme/Platten/Bücher*
gen	*der neuen Filme/Platten/Bücher*
dat	*den neuen Filmen/Platten/Büchern*

Adjectives after *ein/eine* (a):

nom	*ein neuer Film*	*eine neue Platte*	*ein neues Buch*
acc	*einen neuen Film*	*eine neue Platte*	*ein neues Buch*
gen	*eines neuen Films*	*einer neuen Platte*	*eines neuen Buchs*
dat	*einem neuen Film*	*einer neuen Platte*	*einem neuen Buch*

In the plural they always end in "en", e.g. *neuen Filme* (new films), *neuen Platten* etc.

I, you, he, she etc.

I	*ich*	he	*er*	we	*wir*
you	*du, Sie* or *ihr*	she	*sie*	they	*sie*
		it	*es* (also *er* or sie)		

There are three words for "you". *Du* is singular informal. Say *du* to a friend or someone your age or younger. *Ihr* is plural informal. Use it like *du* but when speaking to more than one person. *Sie* is polite (pol) singular and plural. Use if for strangers and older people. It is always written with a capital "S". If in doubt, use *Sie*. Saying *du* or *ihr* to people who don't expect it can be rude.

"It" is *er* when it refers to a (m) noun, *sie* when it refers to a (f) noun, and *es* when it refers to a (n) noun.

Me, you, him, it etc.

Words like "I", "you", or "it" are pronouns (words that replace nouns). In a sentence they do the same jobs as the nouns they replace, so they too have different forms in the various cases:

	I/ me[1]	you	he/ him	she/ her	it
nom	*ich*	*du*	*er*	*sie*	*es*
acc	*mich*	*dich*	*ihn*	*sie*	*es*
dat	*mir*	*dir*	*ihm*	*ihr*	*ihm*

	we/ us	you	you (pol)	they/ them
nom	*wir*	*ihr*	*Sie*	*sie*
acc	*uns*	*euch*	*Sie*	*sie*
acc	*uns*	*euch*	*Ihnen*	*ihnen*

My, your, his etc.

In German "my", "your" etc. change according to the noun they relate to:

with	(m)	(f)	(n) noun
my	*mein*	*meine*	*mein*
your	*dein*	*deine*	*dein*
his, its	*sein*	*seine*	*sein*
her, its	*ihr*	*ihre*	*ihr*
our	*unser*	*unsere*	*unser*
your	*euer*	*eure*	*euer*
their	*ihr*	*ihre*	*ihr*
your (pol)	*Ihr*	*Ihre*	*Ihr*

E.g. *Mein Bruder* (my brother), *meine Schwester* (my sister), etc. *Mein, dein* etc. take the same endings as *ein* in the different cases (see *Ein/eine/ein*).

[1] English pronouns also have different cases: *ich* = I, *mich* = me, *mir* = to me and so on.

Verbs

German verbs have lots of tenses (present, future etc.) but you can get by with two: the present tense for talking about the present and future, and the perfect for talking about the past.

Present tense

In German, most verbs follow one pattern. In the infinitive[1] they end in "en", e.g. hören (to hear). Drop "en" and use the ending you need:

I hear	*ich*	*hör e*
you hear	*du*	*hör st*
he/she/it hears	*er/ sie/es*	*hör t*
we hear	*wir*	*hör en*
you hear	*ihr*	*hör t*
they hear	*sie*	*hör en*
you hear (pol)	*Sie*	*hör en*

Sometimes "e" precedes "t" endings, e.g. *arbeiten* (to work): *er/ihr arbeitet* (he works/you work).

Verbs like *hören* are called weak verbs. Strong verbs have a vowel change with *du* and *er*, e.g. *geben* (to give):

I give	*ich*	*geb e*
you give	*du*	*gib st*
he/she/it gives	*er/ sie/es*	*gib t*
we give	*wir*	*geb en*
you give	*ihr*	*geb t*
they give	*sie*	*geb en*
you give (pol)	*Sie*	*geb en*

Below are useful strong verbs with their *er* (he) forms in brackets. Some strong verbs only have a special past participle, a form needed for making the perfect tense (see Talking about the past), so this is given after the *er* form:

to be	*sein (ist, gewesen)*
to become	*werden (wird, geworden)*
to begin	*beginnen (beginnt, begonnen)*
to come	*kommen (kommt, gekommen)*
to do	*tun (tut, getan)*
to find	*finden (findet, gefunden)*
to go	*gehen (geht, gegangen)*
to go, to drive	*fahren (fährt, gefahren)*
to lie, to be	*liegen, (liegt, gelegen)*
to see	*sehen (sieht, gesehen)*
to stand, to be	*stehen (steht, gestanden)*
to stay	*bleiben (bleibt, geblieben)*

German doesn't distinguish between the two English present tenses (e.g. I drive, I am driving) so *ich fahre* can mean either.

Useful irregular verbs

to be[2]	*sein*	to have/ have got	*haben*
I am	*ich bin*	I have	*ich habe*
you are	*du bist*	you have	*du hast*
he/she/it is	*er/sie/es ist*	he/she/it has	*er/sie/es hat*
we are	*wir sind*	we have	*wir haben*
you are	*ihr seid*	you have	*ihr habt*
they are	*sie sind*	you have	*sie haben*
you (pol) are	*Sie sind*	you (pol) have	*Sie haben*

to have to	*müssen*	to be able to	*können*
I must	*ich muß*	I can	*ich kann*
you must	*du mußt*	you can	*du kannst*
he/she/it must	*er/sie/es muß*	he/she/it can	*er/sie/es kann*
we must	*wir müssen*	we can	*wir können*
you must	*ihr müßt*	you can	*ihr könnt*
they must	*sie müssen*	they can	*sie können*
you (pol) must	*Sie müssen*	you (pol) can	*Sie können*

to want to/ intend to	*wollen*
I want to	*ich will*
you want to	*du willst*
he/she/it wants to	*er/sie/es will*
we want to	*wir wollen*
you want to	*ihr wollt*
they want to	*sie wollen*
you (pol) want to	*Sie wollen*

The last three verbs are handy for making sentences like *Ich muß einen Rucksack kaufen* (I must buy a backpack), *Ich will mit dem Zug fahren* (I want to go by train). The second verb in the sentences (*kaufen* – to buy, *fahren* – to go) is in the infinitive[2] and goes at the end.

Mögen (to like) is another useful irregular verb. The present is used with a noun to say what you like, e.g. *Ich mag Horrorfilme* (I like horror films). Another form is very often used with an infinitive like the verbs above to say what you'd like to do, e.g. *Ich möchte ins Kino gehen* (I'd like to go to the cinema):

I like	*ich mäg*	I'd like	*ich möchte*
you like	*du magst*	you'd like	*du möchtest*
he/she/it likes	*er/sie/es mag*	he/she/it would like	*er/sie/es möchte*
we like	*wir mögen*	we'd like	*wir möchten*
you like	*ihr mögt*	you'd like	*ihr möchten*
they like	*sie mögen*	they'd like	*Sie möchten*
you like (pol)	*Sie mögen*	you'd like (pol)	*Sie möchten*

[1] The infinitive (e.g. in English "to run", "to have") is the form in which verbs are given in the Index and dictionaries. [2] German often uses *stehen* (to stand, to be) and *liegen* (to lie, to be) instead of *sein* for saying where things are, e.g. *Die Flasche steht auf dem Tisch* (The bottle

Talking about the future

In everyday German the present is used, often with *später* (later), *morgen* (tomorrow) etc. to place the action in the future: *Er kauft sich morgen ein Rad* (He's going to buy himself a bike tomorrow, literally "He buys himself etc.").

Talking about the past

The easiest way to talk about the past is to use the perfect tense, e.g. *ich habe getanzt* which can mean "I danced" or "I have danced". It is made with the present of *haben* (to have) + the verb's past participle.

The past participle is made with "ge" + the verb's stem (infinitive[1] less "en" ending) + t, e.g. *hören* (to hear), *gehört* (heard); *tanzen* (to dance), *getanzt* (danced). Past participles go at the end of the sentence, e.g. *Ich habe Fußball gespielt* (I played football).

Some verbs have irregular past participles, e.g. *gehen, gegangen* (to go, went). The most useful are in the list of strong verbs (see Present tense).

Some verbs involving movement or change form the perfect with *sein* (to be), e.g. *er ist gegangen* (he has gone):[3]

to be	*sein (ist, gewesen)*
to become	*werden (wird, geworden)*
to come	*kommen (kommt, gekommen)*
to go/drive	*fahren (fährt, gefahren)*
to stay	*bleiben (bleibt, geblieben)*

Separable verbs

Many common verbs are made of two separate parts: prefix + verb, e.g. *auf* + *machen* (to make) = *aufmachen* (to open). In the infinitive[1], the prefix stays in place: *aufmachen* (to open). In the present tense it goes to the end of the sentence: *ich mache die Tür auf* (I open the door). In the perfect tense it goes to the start of the past participle: *ich habe die Tür aufgemacht* (I have opened the door).

Here are common prefixes with their usual meanings. Verbs that begin with one of these are separable:

ab	(off)	*nach*	(after)
an	(at, on)	*vor*	(before)
auf	(up)	*weg*	(away)
aus	(out)	*zu*	(to)
ein	(in, into)	*zurück*	(back)

Negatives

To make a sentence negative, put *nicht* (not) after the verb, e.g. *ich will nicht* (I don't want to) or with a separable verb: *ich höre nicht zu* (I'm not listening). In the perfect *nicht* precedes the past participle: *Ich habe es nicht getan* (I didn't do it).

To say "not a" you use *kein*, e.g. *Sie ist keine gute Sängerin* (She's not a good singer), *sie hat keine gute Stimme* (she hasn't got a brilliant voice, literally "She has not a brilliant voice"). *Kein* is the negative of *ein* (a) and changes like it, e.g. *kein Mann* (no man), *keine Frau* (no woman) etc. (see *Ein, eine, ein* on page 75).

Other useful negative words include *nie* (never), *niemand* (nobody) and *nichts* (nothing).

Questions

To make questions, you put the subject after the verb, e.g. *Bist du müde?* (Are you tired?) *Haben wir Zeit* (Do we have time?)

Questions can also begin with words like:

how?	*wie?*	where?	*wo?*
how much?	*wieviel?*	which?	*welche?*
what?	*was?*	who?	*wer?*
when?	*wann?*	why?	*warum?*

Prepositions

Prepositions ("with", "on" etc.) are followed by an accusative or dative noun (or pronoun). Some always require the same case, e.g. *ohne* + accusative: *Er ist ohne mich gegangen* (He went without me); *mit* + dative: *Er ist mit mir gegangen* (He went with me). Many prepositions require either the accusative or the dative depending on whether they are indicating movement or static position. When indicating movement, they are followed by the accusative, e.g. *Er ist auf den Tisch gesprungen* (He leapt on the table). When indicating static position (no movement), they require the dative: *Er sitzt auf dem Tisch* (He's sitting on the table).

Here are some useful prepositions with the cases they require:

against	*gegen* (acc)
away from	*weg von* (dat)
behind	*hinter* (acc or dat)
beside	*neben* (acc or dat)
between	*zwischen* (acc or dat)
in	*in* (dat)
in front of	*vor* (acc or dat)
into	*in* (acc)
near	*nahe an* (dat)
on	*auf* (acc or dat)
opposite	*gegenüber* (dat)
out of	*aus* (dat)
over	*über* (acc or dat)
under	*unter* (acc or dat)
through	*durch* (acc)
with	*mit* (dat)
without	*ohne* (acc)

is on the table), *Das Kino liegt an der Ecke* (The cinema is on the corner). [3]In South Germany, Austria and Switzerland, people form the perfect tense with *sein* for lots of verbs.

Numbers, time etc. (French)

Numbers

0	*zéro*	*zeh-roh*
1	*un*	*u(n)*
2	*deux*	*dur*
3	*trois*	*trwa*
4	*quatre*	*katr*
5	*cinq*	*sa(n)k*
6	*six*	*seess*
7	*sept*	*set*
8	*huit*	*weet*
9	*neuf*	*nurf*
10	*dix*	*deess*
11	*onze*	*o(n)z*
12	*douze*	*dooz*
13	*treize*	*trehz*
14	*quatorze*	*katorz*
15	*quinze*	*ka(n)z*
16	*seize*	*sez*
17	*dix-sept*	*dee-set*
18	*dix-huit*	*deez-weet*
19	*dix-neuf*	*deez-nurf*
20	*vingt*	*va(n)*
21	*vingt et un*	*va(n)teh-u(n)*
22	*vingt-deux*	*va(n)-dur*
30	*trente*	*tro(n)t*
31	*trente et un*	*tro(n)teh-u(n)*
40	*quarante*	*ka-ro(n)t*
50	*cinquante*	*sa(n)ko(n)t*
60	*soixante*	*swa-so(n)t*
70	*soixante-dix*	*swa-so(n)t-deess*
71	*soixante et onze*	*swa-so(n)teh-o(n)z*
80	*quatre-vingts*	*katr-va(n)*
81	*quatre-vingt-un*	*katr-va(n)-u(n)*
90	*quatre-vingt-dix*	*katr-va(n)-deess*
91	*quatre-vingt-onze*	*katr-va(n)-o(n)z*
100	*cent*	*so(n)*
101	*cent un*	*so(n) u(n)*
200	*deux cents*	*dur so(n)*
1,000	*mille*	*meel*
100,000	*cent mille*	*so(n) meel*
1,000,000	*un million*	*u(n) meel-yo(n)*

Days and months

Monday	*lundi*	*lu(n)dee*
Tuesday	*mardi*	*mardee*
Wednesday	*mercredi*	*mairkre(r)dee*
Thursday	*jeudi*	*ju(r)dee*
Friday	*vendredi*	*vo(n)dre(r)dee*
Saturday	*samedi*	*samdee*
Sunday	*dimanche*	*deemo(n)sh*
January	*janvier*	*jo(n)vee-eh*
February	*février*	*fev-ree-eh*
March	*mars*	*mahss*
April	*avril*	*a-vreel*
May	*mai*	*my*
June	*juin*	*joo-a(n)*
July	*juillet*	*joo-ee-yeh*
August	*août*	*oot*
September	*septembre*	*sep-to(m)br*
October	*octobre*	*ok-tobr*
November	*novembre*	*nov-o(m)br*
December	*décembre*	*deh-so(m)br*

Time

hour	*l'heure*	*lur*
minute	*la minute*	*la mee-newt*
afternoon	*l'après-midi*	*la-preh-mee-dee*
evening	*le soir*	*le(r) swahr*
midday	*midi*	*mee-dee*
midnight	*minuit*	*mee-new-ee*
What time is it?	*Quelle heure est-il?*	*Kellur-eh-teel?*
It's 1 o'clock.	*Il est une heure.*	*Eel-eh ew-nur.*
It's 2 o'clock.	*Il est deux heures.*	*Eel-eh dur-zur.*
a quarter past two	*deux heures et quart*	*dur-zur eh kar*
half past two	*deux heures et demie*	*dur-zur eh de(r)mee*
a quarter to two	*deux heures moins le quart*	*dur-zur mwa(n) le(r) kar*
five past three	*trois heures cinq*	*trwa-zur sa(n)k*
ten to four	*quatre heures moins dix*	*katr-ur mwa(n) deess*

[1] *Uno* drops the "o" before masculine nouns, e.g. *un libro* (one book).

[2] *Cien* changes into *ciento* when followed by a smaller number.

Numbers, time etc. (Spanish)

Numbers

0	*cero*	th-eh-roh
1	*uno*[1]*/una*	oo-noh/oo-na
2	*dos*	dohs
3	*tres*	trehs
4	*cuatro*	kwa-troh
5	*cinco*	theen-koh
6	*seis*	seh-ees
7	*siete*	syeh-teh
8	*ocho*	oh-tchoh
9	*nueve*	nweh-beh
10	*diez*	dyeh-th
11	*once*	ohn-theh
12	*doce*	doh-theh
13	*trece*	treh-theh
14	*catorce*	ka-tohr-theh
15	*quince*	keen-theh
16	*dieciséis*	dyeh-thee-seh-ees
17	*diecisiete*	dyeh-thee-syeh-teh
18	*dieciocho*	dyeh-thee-oh-tchoh
19	*diecinueve*	dyeh-thee-nweh-beh
20	*veinte*	beh-een-teh
21	*veintiuno*	beh-een-tee-oo-noh
22	*veintidós*	beh-een-tee-dohs
30	*treinta*	treh-een-ta
31	*treinta y uno*	treh-een-ta ee oo-noh
40	*cuarenta*	kwa-rehn-ta
50	*cincuenta*	theen-kwehn-ta
60	*sesenta*	seh-sehn-ta
70	*setenta*	seh-tehn-ta
71	*setenta y uno*	seh-tehn-ta ee oo-noh
80	*ochenta*	oh-tchehn-ta
81	*ochenta y uno*	oh-tchehn-ta ee oo-noh
90	*noventa*	noh-behn-ta
91	*noventa y uno*	noh-behn-ta ee oo-noh
100	*cien, ciento*[2]	th-yehn, th-yehn-toh
101	*ciento uno*	th-yehn-toh oo-noh
200	*doscientos/doscientas*	doh-th-yehn-tohs/doh-th-yehn-tas
1,000	*mil*	meel
100,000	*cien mil*	th-yehn meel
1,000,000	*un millón*	oon meel-yohn

Days and months

Monday	*lunes*	loo-nehs
Tuesday	*martes*	mar-tehs
Wednesday	*miércoles*	myehr-koh-lehs
Thursday	*jueves*	gh-weh-behs
Friday	*viernes*	byehr-nehs
Saturday	*sábado*	sa-ba-doh
Sunday	*domingo*	doh-meen-goh
January	*enero*	eh-neh-roh
February	*febrero*	feh-breh-roh
March	*marzo*	mar-thoh
April	*abril*	a-breel
May	*mayo*	ma-yoh
June	*junio*	ghoo-nyoh
July	*julio*	ghoo-lyoh
August	*agosto*	a-gohs-toh
September	*setiembre, septiembre*	seht-yehm-breh
October	*octubre*	oh-too-breh
November	*noviembre*	noh-byehm-breh
December	*diciembre*	deeth-yehm-breh

Time

hour	*hora*	oh-ra
minute	*minuto*	mee-noo-toh
afternoon	*la tarde*	la tar-deh
evening	*la noche*	la noh-tcheh
midday	*el mediodía*	ehl meh-dyoh-dee-a
midnight	*la medianoche*	la meh-dya-noh-tcheh
What time is it?	*¿Qué hora es?*	¿Keh oh-ra ehs?
It's 1 o'clock.	*Es la una en punto.*	Ehs la oo-na ehn poon-toh.
It's 2 o'clock.	*Son las dos en punto.*	Sohn las dohs ehn poon-toh.
a quarter past two	*las dos y cuarto*	las dohs ee kwar-toh
half past two	*las dos y media*	las dohs ee meh-dya
a quarter to two	*las dos menos cuarto*	las dohs meh-nohs kwar-toh
five past three	*las tres y cinco*	las trehs ee theen-koh
ten to four	*las cuatro menos diez*	las kwa-troh meh-nohs dyeh-th

Numbers, time etc. (Italian)

Numbers

0	*zero*	'tsair-oh
1	*uno/una*	'oo-noh/'oo-na
2	*due*	'doo-eh
3	*tre*[1]	treh
4	*quattro*	'kwat-troh
5	*cinque*	'cheen-kweh
6	*sei*	'seh
7	*sette*	'set-teh
8	*otto*	'ot-toh
9	*nove*	'no-veh
10	*dieci*	dee-'eh-chee
11	*undici*	'oon-dee-chee
12	*dodici*	'doh-dee-chee
13	*tredici*	'treh-dee-chee
14	*quattordici*	kwat-'tohr-dee-chee
15	*quindici*	'kween-dee-chee
16	*sedici*	'seh-dee-chee
17	*diciassette*	dee-chas-'set-teh
18	*diciotto*	dee-'chot-toh
19	*diciannove*	dee-chan-'noh-veh
20	*venti*	'vehn-tee
21	*ventuno*[2]	vehn-'too-noh
22	*ventidue*	vehn-tee-'doo-eh
30	*trenta*	'trehn-ta
31	*trentunoh*	trehn-'too-noh
40	*quaranta*	kwa-'ran-ta
50	*cinquanta*	cheen-'kwan-ta
60	*sessanta*	ses-'san-ta
70	*settanta*	set-'tan-ta
71	*settantuno*	set-tan-'too-noh
80	*ottanta*	ot-'tan-ta
81	*ottantuno*	ot-tan-'too-noh
90	*novanta*	no-'van-ta
91	*novantuno*	no-van-'too-noh
100	*cento*	'chehn-toh
101	*centouno*	'chehn-toh-'oo-noh
200	*duecento*	doo-eh-'chehn-toh
1,000	*mille*	'meel-leh
100,000	*cento mila*	'chehn-toh 'meel-la
1,000,000	*un milione*	oon mee-lee-'oh-neh

Days and months

Monday	*lunedì*	loo-neh-'dee
Tuesday	*martedì*	mar-teh-'dee
Wednesday	*mercoledì*	mehr-coh-leh-'dee
Thursday	*giovedì*	joh-veh-'dee
Friday	*venerdì*	ve-nehr-'dee
Saturday	*sabato*	'sa-ba-toh
Sunday	*domenica*	do-'meh-nee-ca
January	*gennaio*	jen-'na-ee-oh
February	*febbraio*	feb-bra-ee-oh
March	*marzo*	'mar-tsoh
April	*aprile*	a-'pree-leh
May	*maggio*	'maj-joh
June	*giugno*	'joo-nyoh
July	*luglio*	'loo-lyoh
August	*agosto*	a-'gos-toh
September	*settembre*	set-'tem-breh
October	*ottobre*	ot-'toh-breh
November	*novembre*	no-'vem-breh
December	*dicembre*	dee-'chem-breh

Time

hour	*ora*	'oh-ra
minute	*minuto*	mee-'noo-toh
afternoon	*pomeriggio*	poh-mehr-'eej-joh
evening	*sera*	'sehr-a
midday	*mezzogiorno*	met-tsoh-'johr-noh
midnight	*mezzanotte*	met-tsa-'not-teh
What time is it?	*Che ore sono?*	Keh 'oh-ra 'soh-noh?
It's 1 o'clock.	*É l'una.*	Eh 'loo-na.
It's 2 o'clock.	*Sono le due.*	'So-no leh 'doo-eh.
a quarter past two	*le due e un quarto*	leh 'doo-eh eh oon 'kwar-toh
half past two	*le due e mezza*	leh 'doo-eh eh 'met-tsa
a quarter to two	*le due meno un quarto*	leh 'doo-eh 'meh-no oon 'kwar-toh
five past three	*le tre e cinque*	leh treh eh 'cheen-kweh
ten to four	*le quattro meno dieci*	leh 'kwat-troh 'meh-noh dee-'eh-chee

[1] *Tre* changes to *tré* when added to another number, e.g. *ventitré* (twenty-three).

[2] The vowel at the end of a number is ommitted when *uno* or *otto* is added.

Numbers, time etc. (German)

Numbers

0 *null* nool	14 *vierzehn* fear-tsayn	60 *sechzig* zech-tsich
1 *eins* eynss	15 *fünfzehn* fewnf-tsayn	70 *siebzig* zeeb-tsich
2 *zwei* tsvy	16 *sechzehn* zechss-tsayn	71 *einundsiebzig* eyn-oont-zeeb-tsich
3 *drei* dry	17 *siebzehn* zeeb-tsayn	80 *achtzig* ahcht-tsich
4 *vier* fear	18 *achtzehn* ahcht-tsayn	81 *einundachtzig* eyn-oont-ahcht-tsich
5 *fünf* fewnf	19 *neunzehn* noyn-tsayn	90 *neunzig* noyn-tsich
6 *sechs* zechss	20 *zwanzig* tsvan-zich	91 *einundneunzig* eyn-oont-noyn-tsich
7 *sieben* zee-ben	21 *einundzwanzig* eyn-oont-tsvan-zich	100 *(ein) hundert* (eyn) hoon-dert
8 *acht* ahcht	22 *zweiundzwanzig* tsvy-oont-tsvan-zich	101 *hunderteins* hoon-dert-eynss
9 *neun* noyn	30 *dreißig* dry-sich	200 *zweihundert* tsvy-hoon-dert
10 *zehn* tsayn	31 *einunddreißig* eyn-oont-dry-sich	1,000 *(ein) tausend* (eyn) towzent
11 *elf* elf	40 *vierzig* fear-tsich	100,000 *hunderttausend* hoondert-towzent
12 *zwölf* tsvu(r)lf	50 *fünfzig* fewnf-tsich	1,000,000 *eine Million* eyne(r) mill-yohn
13 *dreizehn* dry-tsayn		

Days and months

Monday	*Montag* mon-tak	January	*Januar* yanoo-ahr	July	*Juli* yoolee
Tuesday	*Dienstag* deenss-tak	February	*Februar* febroo-ahr	August	*August* ow-goost
Wednesday	*Mittwoch* mit-voch	March	*März* mairts	September	*September* september
Thursday	*Donnerstag* donnerss-tak	April	*April* a-preel	October	*Oktober* oktober
Friday	*Freitag* fry-tak	May	*Mai* my	November	*November* november
Saturday	*Samstag* zamss-tak	June	*Juni* yoonee	December	*Dezember* detsember
Sunday	*Sonntag* zon-tak				

Time

hour	*die Stunde* dee shtoonde(r)	It's 1 o'clock.	*Es ist ein Uhr.* Ess isst eyn oor.
minute	*die Minute* dee mi-noo-te(r)	It's 2 o'clock.	*Es ist zwei Uhr.* Ess isst tsvy oor.
afternoon	*der Nachmittag* derr nach-mittak	a quarter past two	*viertel nach zwei* fear-tel nach tsvy
evening	*der Abend* derr ah-bent	half past two	*halb drei* halp dry
midday	*Mittag* mittak	a quarter to two	*viertel vor zwei* fear-tel for tsvy
midnight	*Mitternacht* mitter-nacht	five past three	*fünf nach drei* fewnf nach dry
What time is it?	*Wie spät ist es?/Wieviel Uhr ist es?* Vee shpet isst ess?/Vee-feel oor isst ess?	ten to four	*zehn vor vier* tsayn for fear

Index

The index lists the most essential words. Most words are followed by a page number telling you where they appear in the book.

If you can't find the word you want, look up a relevant entry, e.g. to find "cauliflower" look under "vegetables".

Adjectives with two forms are given twice: (m) followed by (f) (see pages 62, 66, 70 and 74) and verbs are in the infinitive.

If the gender of a noun is not clear, (m), (f) or (n) is placed in brackets after it. In Italian, if the noun ends in "o" it is (m), if it ends in "a" it is (f), unless it is indicated otherwise.

In the German column, nouns have their plurals in brackets. (¨) means the plural has an umlaut, (–) means it doesn't change (see page 74). When German nouns are plural only, this is indicated by pl. after the gender, e.g. die Aspirin (n pl).

	F	S	I	G
bill, 16	*l'addition (f)*	*la cuenta*	*il conto*	*die Rechnung(en)*
black	*noir/noire*	*negro/negra*	*nero/nera*	*schwarz*
blue	*bleu/bleuie*	*azul*	*blu*	*blau*
boarding pass, 60	*la carte d'embarquement*	*la tarjeta de embarque*	*la carta d'imbarco*	*die Bordkarte(n)*
boat, 47	*le bateau*	*la barca*	*la barca*	*das Boot(e)*
to book, 60/61	*réserver*	*reservar*	*prenotare*	*reservieren*
book	*le livre*	*el libro*	*il libro*	*das Buch(¨er)*
to borrow, 18/19	*emprunter*	*prestar*	*prendere a prestito, farsi prestare*	*borgen, leihen*
bottle, 26	*la bouteille*	*la botella*	*la bottiglia*	*die Flasche(n)*
boy	*le garçon*	*el chico*	*il ragazzo*	*der Junge(n)*
boyfriend, 54	*le petit ami, le Jules***	*el novio, el chico**	*il ragazzo*	*der Alte, der Freund(e)*
bread, 30	*le pain*	*el pan*	*il pane*	*das Brot*
breakfast, 16/17, 18/19	*le petit déjeuner*	*el desayuno*	*la colazione*	*das Frühstück*
bridge, 9	*le pont*	*el puente*	*il ponte*	*die Brücke(n)*
Britain	*la Grande-Bretagne*	*la Gran Bretaña*	*la Gran Bretagna*	*das Großbritannien*
brother	*le frère*	*el hermano*	*il fratello*	*der Bruder(¨)*
brown	*marron, brun/brune*	*marrón*	*marrone*	*braun*
bus, 10/11	*le bus, l'autobus (m)*	*el autobús*	*l'autobus (m)*	*der Bus(se)*
bus station, 6, 10	*la gare routière*	*la estación de autobuses*	*la stazione degli autobus*	*der Busbahnhof(¨e)*
bus stop, 10	*l'arrêt d'autobus (m)*	*la parada de autobús*	*la fermata dell'autobus*	*die Bushaltestelle(n)*
butter, 30	*le beurre*	*la mantequilla*	*il burro*	*die Butter*
to buy, 10/11	*acheter*	*comprar*	*comprare*	*kaufen*
bye, 4	*salut*	*adiós*	*ciao*	*tschüs*
café, 26	*le café, le bar*	*el café*	*il bar*	*das Café(s)*
to call	*appeler*	*llamar*	*chiamare*	*anrufen*
camera, 59	*l'appareil-photo (m)*	*la cámara fotográfica*	*la macchina fotografica*	*der Fotoapparat(e)*
to camp, 20/21	*camper*	*acampar*	*campeggiare*	*zelten*
camping gas cannister, 21	*la cartouche de camping-gaz*	*la botella de camping gas*	*il fornellino da campeggio*	*der Campinggas Kanister*
campsite, 6	*le camping*	*el camping*	*l'area di campeggio*	*der Campingplatz (¨e)*
to cancel, 60/61	*annuler*	*cancelar*	*annullare*	*stornieren*
can opener, 21	*l'ouvre-boîte (m)*	*el abrelatas*	*l'apriscatole (f)*	*der Dosenöffner(-)*
car, 12, 14, 15	*la voiture*	*el coche*	*la macchina, l'auto (f)*	*das Auto(s)*

*slang. **rude.

	F	S	I	G
car park, 9	*le parking*	*el aparcamiento*	*il parcheggio*	*der Parkplatz(¨e)*
caravan, 20	*la caravane*	*la caravana*	*la roulotte*	*der Wohnwagen(-)*
cash dispenser, 22	*le distributeur automatique*	*el cajero automático*	*il bancomat*	*der Geldautomat (en)*
cashier's desk, 22	*la caisse*	*la caja*	*il banco, la cassa*	*die Kasse(n)*
castle, 42	*le château*	*el castillo*	*il castello*	*das Schloß (Schlösser)*
cave, 42	*la grotte*	*la cueva*	*la grotta*	*die Höhle(n)*
to change, 10/11, 22/23, 60/61	*changer*	*cambiar*	*cambiare*	*umtauschen, ändern*
changing room, 36/37	*la cabine d'essayage*	*el probador*	*lo spogliatoio*	*die Umkleidekabine (n)*
to check in, 60/61	*se presenter*	*presentarse*	*fare il check in*	*einchecken*
cheese, 30	*le fromage*	*el queso*	*il formaggio*	*der Käse(-)*
chemist, 33	*la pharmacie*	*la farmacia*	*la farmacia*	*die Apotheke(n), die Drogerie(n)*
chips, 30	*les frites (f)*	*las patatas fritas*	*le patate fritte*	*die Fritten (f pl), die Pommes frites*
chocolate, 31	*le chocolat*	*el chocolate*	*il cioccolato*	*die Schokolade(n)*
church, 42	*l'église (f)*	*la iglesia*	*la chiesa*	*die Kirche(n)*
cigarette, 34	*la cigarette*	*el cigarrillo*	*la sigaretta*	*die Zigarette(n)*
cinema, 48/49	*le cinéma*	*el cine*	*il cinema*	*das Kino(s)*
closed	*fermé/fermée*	*cerrado/cerrada*	*chiuso/a/i/e*	*geschlossen*
clothes, 36	*les vêtements (m)*	*la ropa*	*l'abbigliamento (m pl)*	*die Kleider (n pl)*
code number (telephone), 25	*l'indicatif (m)*	*el prefijo*	*il prefisso telefonico*	*die Vorwahl(en)*
coffee, 27	*le café*	*el café*	*il caffè*	*der Kaffee*
coke, 31	*le coca*	*la coca-cola*	*la coca cola*	*die Cola*
cold, 20	*froid/froide*	*frío/fría*	*freddo/fredda*	*kalt*
a cold, 56	*le rhume*	*el resfriado*	*il raffreddore*	*die Erkältung(en)*
colour, 36/37	*la couleur*	*el color*	*il colore*	*die Farbe(n)*
to come	*venir*	*venir*	*venire*	*kommen*
concert, 48	*le concert*	*el concierto*	*il concerto*	*das Konzert(e)*
condom, 35	*le préservatif*	*el condón*	*il preservativo, il profilattico*	*das Präservativ(e), das Kondom(e)*
to confirm, 60/61	*confirmer*	*confirmar*	*confermare*	*bestätigen*
constipated, 57	*constipé/constipée*	*estreñimiento*	*stitico/stitica*	*an Verstopfung leiden*
contact lens, 35	*le verre de contact*	*la lente de contacto*	*la lente a contatto*	*die Kontaktlinse(n)*
controls, 12/13	*les commandes (f)*	*los mandos*	*i controlli*	*die Schalter (m pl)*
cooker	*la cuisinière*	*la cocina*	*la cucina*	*der Herd(e)*
to cost, 14/15	*coûter*	*costar*	*costare*	*kosten*
cotton, 34	*le fil*	*el hilo*	*il cotone*	*der Faden*

	F	S	I	G
crash helmet	*le casque*	*el casco*	*il casco*	*der Sturzhelm(e)*
credit card, 22, 58	*la carte de crédit*	*la tarjeta de crédito*	*la carta di credito*	*die Kreditkarte(n)*
crisps, 30	*les chips (f)*	*las patatas fritas*	*le patatine*	*die Chips (n pl)*
to cross, 8	*traverser*	*cruzar*	*attraversare*	*überqueren*
crossroads, 9	*le carrefour*	*el cruce*	*l'incrocio*	*die Kreuzung(en)*
customs, 61	*la douane*	*la aduana*	*la dogana*	*der Zoll*
to cycle	*faire de la bicyclette*	*andar en bicicleta*	*andare in bicicletta*	*radfahren*
to dance, 48/49, 50/51	*danser*	*bailar*	*ballare*	*tanzen*
dark (colour)	*foncé/foncée*	*oscuro*	*scuro/scura*	*dunkel*
day, 12/13	*le jour*	*el día*	*il giorno*	*der Tag(e)*
to delay, 60/61	*retarder*	*retrasar*	*ritardare, rimandare*	*verspäten*
dentist, 56/57	*le dentiste*	*el/la dentista*	*il/la dentista*	*der Zahnarzt(¨e)*
deodorant, 34	*le déodorant*	*el desodorante*	*il deodorante*	*der Deodorant(s),*
departure gate, 60	*la porte (de départ)*	*la puerta de salida*	*l'uscita*	*der Ausgang(¨e)*
dessert, 27	*le dessert*	*el postre*	*il dolce*	*die Nachspeise(n), der Nachtisch(e)*
to develop (film), 32/33	*développer*	*revelar*	*sviluppare*	*entwickeln*
diarrhoea, 56	*la diarrhée*	*la diarrea*	*la diarrea*	*der Durchfall*
dictionary	*le dictionnaire*	*el diccionario*	*il dizionario*	*das Wörterbuch(¨er)*
diesel, 13	*le diesel*	*el gasóleo, el gasoil*	*il diesel*	*der Diesel*
dinner, 16	*le dîner*	*la cena*	*la cena*	*das Abendessen(-)*
(telephone) directory, 24	*l'annuaire (m)*	*el listín telefónico*	*l'elenco telefonico*	*das Telefonbuch(¨er)*
directory enquiries, 24	*les renseignements (m)*	*la información*	*le informazioni telefoniche*	*die Auskunft*
disco, 48	*la boîte, la discothèque*	*la discoteca*	*la discoteca*	*die Disco(s)*
dizzy, 57	*la tête qui tourne*	*mareado/mareada*	*vertiginoso*	*schwindlig*
to do	*faire*	*hacer*	*fare*	*machen*
doctor, 56/57	*le médecin, le docteur*	*el médico*	*il medico*	*der Arzt(¨e)*
drink, 28/31, 48/49, 50/51	*la boisson*	*la bebida*	*la bibita*	*das Getränk(e)*
to drink	*boire*	*beber*	*bere*	*trinken*
to drive	*conduire*	*conducir*	*condurre*	*Auto fahren*
driving licence, 12	*le permis de conduire*	*el carnet de conducir*	*la patente di guida*	*der Führerschein(e)*

	F	S	I	G
duty free shop, 61	*la boutique hors taxe*	*la tienda libre de impuestos*	*il negozio di duty free*	*das Duty free shop*
to eat eating, 26/27, 28/29, 30/31	*manger*	*comer*	*mangiare*	*essen*
electric socket, 21	*la prise de courant*	*el enchufe*	*la presa elettrica*	*die Steckdose(n)*
emergencies, 58/59				
engaged (telephone), 25	*occupé*	*comunica*	*occupato*	*besetzt*
English, 4/5, 24/25, 40	*l'anglais (m)*	*el inglés*	*l'inglese (m)*	*das Englisch*
enquiries, 24	*le bureau de renseignements*	*la información*	*le informazioni*	*die Auskunft, die Information*
entrance	*l'entrée (f)*	*la entrada*	*l'entrata*	*der Eingang(¨e)*
envelope, 23	*l'enveloppe (f)*	*el sobre*	*la busta*	*der Umschlag(¨e)*
essay, 41	*la dissertation*	*el trabajo escrito*	*il tema*	*der Aufsatz(¨e)*
eurocheques, 22	*les eurochèques (m)*	*los eurocheques*	*gli eurocheques*	*die Euroschecks (m pl)*
evening, 48/49	*le soir*	*la noche*	*la sera*	*der Abend(e)*
exam, 41	*l'examen (m)*	*el examen*	*l'esame (m)*	*die Prüfung(en)*
exchange rate, 22	*le cours de change*	*la tarifa de cambio*	*il cambio*	*der Wechselkurs(e)*
excuse me, 5	*pardon*	*perdone/ perdona*	*mi scusi*	*entschuldigung*
exhibition, 42	*l'exposition (f)*	*la exposición*	*la mostra*	*die Ausstellung(en)*
exit	*la sortie*	*la salida*	*l'uscita*	*der Ausgang(¨e)*
family	*la famille*	*la familia*	*la famiglia*	*die Familie(n)*
far, 6/7, 8/9	*loin*	*lejos*	*lontano*	*weit*
fare, 12/13	*le tarif*	*el precio, la tarifa*	*la tariffa*	*der Fahrpreis(e)*
father	*le père*	*el padre*	*il padre*	*der Vater(¨)*
ferry, 60	*le ferry*	*el barco*	*il traghetto*	*die Fähre(n)*
film (camera), 32/33	*la pellicule*	*el carrete*	*il rullino*	*der Film(e)*
film (cinema), 48	*le film*	*la película*	*il film*	*der Film(e)*
fire	*le feu*	*la hoguera, el fuego*	*il falò, il fuoco, l'incendio*	*das Feuer(-)*
first, 8/9	*premier/ première*	*primero/primera*	*primo/prima*	*erste*
fish, 30	*le poisson*	*el pescado*	*il pesce*	*der Fisch(e)*
to fix	*réparer*	*reparar*	*riparare*	*reparieren*
flight, 60/61	*le vol*	*el vuelo*	*il volo*	*der Flug(¨e)*
to follow, 8/9	*suivre*	*seguir*	*seguire*	*folgen, verfolgen*
food, 26/27, 28/29, 30/31	*la cuisine*	*la comida*	*il cibo*	*das Essen*
French, 40	*le français*	*el francés*	*il francese*	*das Französisch*

	F	S	I	G
friend, mate, 55	*l'ami/l'amie, un pote**	*el amigo/ la amiga, el/la colega**	*l'amico/amica*	*der Freund(e)/ die Freundin(nen)*
fruit, 28	*les fruits (m pl)*	*la fruta*	*la frutta*	*das Obst*
fruit juice, 31	*le jus de fruit*	*el zumo de fruta*	*il succo di frutta*	*der Fruchtsaft(¨e)*
full board, 17	*pension*	*pensión completa*	*pensione completa*	*Vollpension*
full, 17	*complet*	*completo/ completa*	*al completo*	*belegt*
game (sport), 45	*la partie*	*la partida*	*la partita*	*das Spiel(e)*
garage, 14/15	*le garage*	*el taller*	*l'autofficina*	*die Werkstatt(¨en)*
German, 40	*l'allemand (m)*	*el alemán*	*il tedesco*	*das Deutsch*
girl	*la fille*	*la chica*	*la ragazza*	*das Mädchen(-)*
girlfriend, 55	*la petite amie, une nana***	*la novia, la chica*, la niña**	*la ragazza*	*die Freundin(nen), die Alte***
glass, 26	*le verre*	*el vaso*	*il bicchiere*	*das Glas(¨er)*
to go, 65, 68, 72, 76	*aller*	*ir*	*andare*	*gehen*
to go out with, 52/53	*sortir avec*	*salir con*	*stare insieme, uscire con*	*gehen mit*
goodbye, 4	*au revoir*	*adiós*	*arrivederci*	*auf Wiedersehen*
good evening, 4	*bonsoir*	*buenas tardes*	*buona sera*	*guten Abend*
good morning, 4	*bonjour*	*buenos días*	*buon giorno*	*guten Morgen*
good night, 4	*bonne nuit*	*buenas noches*	*buona notte*	*gute Nacht*
green	*vert/verte*	*verde*	*verde*	*grün*
grey	*gris/grise*	*gris*	*grigio/grigia*	*grau*
guest house, 17	*la chambre d'hôte*	*la pensión*	*la pensione*	*die Pension(en)*
guide book, 43	*le guide*	*la guía*	*la guida turistica*	*der Führer(-)*
guided tour, 42/43	*la visite guidée*	*el recorrido con guía*	*la visita guidata*	*die Führungen (f pl)*
hairdryer, 19	*le sèche-cheveux*	*el secador*	*l'asciugacapelli (m)*	*der Fön(s)*
half board, 17	*demi-pension*	*media pensión*	*mezza pensione*	*Halbpension*
handbag, 59	*le sac à main*	*el bolso*	*la borsetta*	*die Handtasche(n)*
hand luggage, 61	*les bagages à main*	*el equipaje de mano*	*i bagagli a mano (pl)*	*das Handgepäck*
to have, 64, 68, 72, 76	*avoir*	*tener*	*avere*	*haben*
headache, 57	*le mal de tête*	*el dolor de cabeza*	*il mal di testa*	*die Kopfschmerzen (pl)*
hello, 4	*bonjour*	*hola*	*salve*	*hallo*
Help!, 58/59	*Au secours!*	*¡Ayuda!*	*Aiuto!*	*Hilfe!*
to help, 6/7, 18/19	*aider*	*ayudar*	*aiutare*	*helfen*

***slang. **rude.**

	F	S	I	G
here, 12/13, 26/27, 52/53, 57	*ici*	*aquí*	*qui, qua*	*hier*
Hi!, 4	*salut*	*hola*	*ciao*	*hi, hallo*
to hire, 12/13, 46/47	*louer*	*alquilar*	*noleggiare*	*vermieten, mieten*
to hitch, 13	*faire du stop*	*hacer autostop*	*fare l'autostop*	*trampen*
homework, 41	*les devoirs (m pl)*	*los deberes*	*i compiti (pl)*	*die Hausaufgaben (n pl)*
hospital	*l'hôpital (m)*	*el hospital*	*l'ospedale (m)*	*das Krankenhaus (¨er)*
hot, 20	*chaud/chaude*	*calor/caliente*	*caldo/calda*	*warm, heiß*
hotel, 6, 17	*l'hôtel(m)*	*el hotel*	*l'albergo, l'hotel (m)*	*das Hotel(s)*
hour, 38/39	*l'heure (f)*	*la hora*	*l'ora*	*die Stunde(n)*
house	*la maison*	*la casa*	*la casa*	*das Haus(¨er)*
how	*comment*	*cómo*	*come*	*wie*
How are you?	*Comment allez-vous?*	*¿Cómo está?/ ¿Cómo estás?*	*Come stai/sta?*	*Wie geht es Ihnen?*
How many?	*Combien?*	*¿Cuántos?/ ¿Cuántas?*	*Quanti?*	*Wieviele?*
How much?, 5	*Combien?*	*¿Cuánto/ ¿Cuánta?*	*Quanto?*	*Wieviel?*
Hurry up!, 54/55	*Dépêche-toi!*	*¡Date prisa!*	*Sbrigati!, Fai presto!, Muoviti!*	*Beeil dich!*
to hurt, 57	*faire mal à*	*doler*	*far male*	*weh tun*
ice cream, 31	*la glace*	*el helado*	*il gelato*	*das Eis*
illness, 56/57, 58/59				
in	*dans*	*en, dentro*	*in, a, fra*	*in*
to include	*comprendre*	*incluir*	*includere*	*einschließen*
information, 42/43	*l'information (f)*	*la información*	*l'informazione(f)*	*die Information, die Auskunft*
insect repellent, 34	*la lotion antimoustique*	*la loción contra insectos*	*la lozione anti-insetti*	*das Insekten-schutzmittel(-)*
insurance certificate, 15	*le certificat d'assurance*	*la póliza de seguro*	*il certificato di assicurazione*	*der Ver-sicherungs-nachweis(e)*
iron, 19	*le fer à repasser*	*la plancha*	*il ferro da stiro*	*das Bügeleisen (-)*
Italian, 40	*l'italien (m)*	*el italiano*	*l'italiano*	*das Italienisch*
job, 38/39	*le travail*	*el trabajo*	*il lavoro*	*der Job(s)*
journey	*le voyage*	*el viaje*	*il viaggio*	*die Reise(n), die Fahrt(en)*
key, 16, 18/19	*la clé*	*la llave*	*la chiave*	*der Schlüssel(-)*
to kiss, 52/53	*embrasser*	*besar*	*baciare*	*küssen*
to know	*savoir*	*saber*	*sapere*	*wissen*

	F	S	I	G
to know someone, 52/53	*connaître*	*conocer*	*conoscere*	*kennen*
large, 37	*grand/grande*	*grande*	*grande*	*groß*
last, 10/11	*le dernier, la dernière*	*último/última*	*l'ultimo/l'ultima*	*letzte*
to learn	*apprendre*	*aprender*	*imparare*	*lernen*
to leave (depart)	*partir*	*salir*	*partire*	*abfahren*
left, 8	*à gauche*	*izquierda*	*sinistro/sinistra*	*links*
lecture, 41	*la conférence*	*la conferencia*	*la conferenza, la lezione*	*das Vorlesung(en)*
lecturer, 41	*le prof, le maître de conférences*	*el profesor/ la profesora*	*il docente*	*der Dozent(en)/ die Dozentin(nen)*
lesson (school), 41	*le cours*	*la lección*	*la lezione*	*die Stunde(n)*
lesson (sports), 46/47	*la leçon*	*la lección*	*la lezione*	*die Stunde(n)*
letter, 22/23	*la lettre*	*la carta*	*la lettera*	*der Brief(e)*
library, 40/41	*la bibliothèque*	*la biblioteca*	*la biblioteca*	*die Bücherei(en)*
light (colour)	*clair/claire*	*claro*	*chiaro/chiara*	*hell/helle*
to like	*aimer*	*gustar*	*piacere*	*mögen, gern haben*
to like (doing), 44	*aimer*	*gustar*	*piacere*	*gern tun*
to listen, 48/49	*écouter*	*escuchar*	*ascoltare*	*hören*
to look, 32	*regarder*	*mirar*	*guardare*	*sich umsehen*
to lose, 58	*perdre*	*perder*	*perdere*	*verlieren*
lost, 6/7	*perdu/perdue*	*perdido/perdida*	*perduto*	*verloren*
lunch, 16	*le déjeuner*	*la comida*	*il pranzo*	*das Mittagessen(-)*
lunchbreak, 39	*la pause-déjeuner*	*la hora de la comida*	*l'intervallo per il pranzo*	*die Mittagspause(n)*
Madam, 4	*Madame*	*señora*	*Signora*	*Frau*
main course, 27	*le plat principal*	*el segundo plato*	*la portata principale*	*das Hauptgericht(e)*
main road, 9	*la route principale*	*la carretera principal*	*la strada principale*	*die Hauptstraße*
man	*l'homme (m)*	*el hombre*	*l'uomo*	*der Mann(¨er)*
map, 6/7, 43	*le plan, la carte*	*el mapa*	*la carta*	*der Plan(¨e), die Landkarte(n)*
market, 28/29, 33	*le marché*	*el mercado*	*il mercato*	*der Markt(¨e)*
match (sports), 45	*le match*	*el partido*	*la partita*	*das Spiel(e)*
matches, 20	*les allumettes (f pl)*	*las cerillas (pl)*	*i fiammiferi (pl)*	*die Streichhölzer (n pl)*
meal	*le repas*	*la comida*	*il pasto*	*das Essen(-)*
meat, 30, 31	*la viande*	*la carne*	*la carne*	*das Fleisch*
medium, 37	*moyen/moyenne*	*mediano/ mediana*	*medio/media*	*medium*
to meet, 52/53	*se retrouver, rencontrer*	*encontrarse*	*vedersi*	*abholen, sich treffen*
menu, 26/27	*la carte, le menu*	*el menú*	*il menù*	*die Karte(n)*
milk, 31	*le lait*	*la leche*	*il latte*	*die Milch*

	F	S	I	G
Miss, 4	*Mademoiselle*	*señorita*	*Signorina*	*Fräulein*
to miss (transport), 58/59	*rater*	*perder*	*perdere*	*verpassen, versäumen*
money, 22/23	*l'argent (m)*	*el dinero*	*i soldi (pl)*	*das Geld*
month	*le mois*	*el mes*	*il mese*	*der Monat(e)*
moped, 12	*un vélomoteur*	*la motocicleta*	*il motorino*	*das Moped(s)*
morning	*le matin*	*la mañana*	*il mattino*	*der Morgen*
mosquito bites	*la piqûre de moustique*	*las picaduras de mosquito (pl)*	*le punture di zanzara (pl)*	*der Mückenstich(e)*
mother	*la mère*	*la madre*	*la madre*	*die Mutter(¨)*
motorbike, 12	*la moto*	*la moto*	*la moto*	*das Motorrad(¨er)*
motorway, 9	*l'autoroute (f)*	*la autopista*	*l'autostrada*	*die Autobahn(en)*
Mr, 4	*Monsieur*	*señor*	*Signor*	*Herr*
Mrs, 4	*Madame*	*señora*	*Signora*	*Frau*
museum, 42	*le musée*	*el museo*	*il museo*	*das Museum (Museen)*
music, 48/49	*la musique*	*la música*	*la musica*	*die Musik*
My name is..., 50	*Je m'appelle...*	*Me llamo...*	*Mi chiamo...*	*Ich heiße...*
name, 50	*le nom*	*el nombre*	*il nome*	*der Name(n)*
nasty, 52/53	*mauvais/ mauvaise, vache**	*horrible*	*antipatico/ antipatica, cattivo/cattiva*	*gemein*
near, 6/7, 24/25	*près de*	*cerca de*	*vicino a*	*nah*
needle, 35	*l'aiguille (f)*	*la aguja*	*l'ago*	*die Nadel(n)*
newspaper, 34	*le journal*	*el periódico*	*il giornale*	*die Zeitung(en)*
nice (OK), 53	*sympa*	*simpático/ simpática*	*simpatico/a, passabile*	*nett*
night, 4, 16/17, 20/21	*la nuit*	*la noche*	*la notte*	*die Nacht(¨e)*
nightclub, 48	*une boîte (de nuit)*	*el club nocturno, la disco*	*il locale notturno, il night*	*die Bar(s), die Disco(s)*
no, 5	*non*	*no*	*no*	*nein*
no smoking, 61	*non-fumeurs*	*no fumadores*	*vietato fumare*	*Nichtraucher*
number, 24/25	*le numéro*	*el número*	*il numero*	*die Nummer(n)*
oil, 13	*l'huile (f)*	*el aceite*	*l'olio*	*das Öl*
OK, 20/21, 54	*bien*	*simpático/ simpática, bien*	*OK*	*nett*
on	*sur*	*en, encima*	*su, sopra*	*auf*
to open	*ouvrir*	*abrir*	*aprire*	*aufmachen*
operator, 24	*l'opératrice (f)*	*la operadora*	*il centralino*	*die Vermittlung*
opposite, 8	*en face de*	*enfrente de*	*di fronte*	*gegenüber*
or	*ou*	*o*	*o*	*oder*
palace, 42	*le palais*	*el palacio*	*il palazzo*	*der Palast*
parcel, 22/23	*le colis*	*el paquete*	*il pacco*	*das Paket(e)*
Pardon?, 5	*Pardon?*	*¿Cómo?, ¿Qué?*	*Come?, Scusi?*	*Wie bitte?*
parents	*les parents (m)*	*los padres (pl)*	*i genitori (pl)*	*die Eltern*
party, 49	*la fête*	*la fiesta*	*la festa*	*die Fete*

*slang

	F	S	I	G
passport, 59, 60	*le passeport*	*el pasaporte*	*il passaporto*	*der Paß (Pässe)*
to pay, 32/33, 38/39	*payer*	*pagar*	*pagare*	*bezahlen*
pen, 34	*le stylo*	*el bolígrafo*	*la penna*	*der Stift(e)*
period, 56	*les règles (f)*	*el período, la regla*	*le mestruazioni (pl)*	*die Tage*
petrol, 13	*l'essence (f)*	*la gasolina*	*la benzina*	*das Benzin*
petrol station, 13	*la station-service*	*la gasolinera*	*il benzinaio*	*die Tankstelle(n)*
phone, 24/25	*le téléphone*	*el teléfono*	*il telefono*	*das Telefon(e)*
phone box, 24/25	*la cabine téléphonique*	*la cabina*	*la cabina telefonica*	*die Telefonzelle(n)*
phone number, 24/25	*le numéro de téléphone*	*el número de teléfono*	*il numero di telefono*	*die (Telefon) nummer(n)*
photograph, 42/43	*la photo*	*la foto*	*la fotografia*	*das Foto(s)*
the pill, 57	*la pilule*	*el anticonceptivo*	*la pillola*	*die Pille*
pink	*rose*	*rosa*	*rosa*	*rosa*
plasters, 34	*les sparadraps (m pl)*	*las tiritas (pl)*	*i cerotti (pl)*	*die Pflaster(n pl)*
platform, 11	*le quai*	*el andén*	*il binario*	*der Bahnsteig (e)*
to play (sport), 45	*jouer*	*jugar*	*giocare*	*spielen*
please, 5	*s'il vous plaît, s'il te plaît*	*por favor*	*per favore, per piacere*	*bitte*
police, 58/59	*la police*	*la policía*	*la polizia*	*die Polizei*
(woman) police officer, 58/59	*l'officier de police femme (m)*	*la mujer policía*	*la poliziotta*	*die Polizistin*
police station, 58/59	*le commissariat de police*	*la comisaría de policía*	*il posto di polizia*	*die Polizei-wache(n)*
port, 60	*le port*	*el puerto*	*il porto*	*der Hafen(¨)*
postbox, 23	*la boîte aux lettres*	*el buzón*	*la buca delle lettere*	*der Briefkasten (¨)*
postcard, 23	*la carte postale*	*la postal*	*la cartolina*	*die Postkarte (n)*
poste restante, 23	*poste restante*	*lista de correos*	*fermoposta*	*postlagernd*
post office, 7	*la poste, les PTT (f)*	*la oficina de correos, correos*	*l'ufficio postale*	*die Post, das Postamt (¨er)*
pregnant	*enceinte*	*encinta*	*incinta*	*schwanger*
puncture, 14/15	*la crevaison*	*el pinchazo*	*la foratura, la puntura*	*der Platten*
purse	*le porte-monnaie*	*el monedero*	*il borsellino, il porta monete*	*das Portemon-naie(s)*
to put	*mettre*	*poner*	*mettere, posare*	*stellen, legen*
railway station, 6, 10	*la gare*	*la estación de tren*	*la stazione ferroviaria*	*der Bahnhof(¨e)*
razor, 35	*le rasoir*	*la maquinilla de afeitar*	*il rasoio*	*der Rasier-apparat(e)*
red	*rouge*	*rojo/roja*	*rosso/rossa*	*rot*
(by) registered post, 23	*en recommandé*	*por correo certificado*	*per raccomandata*	*per Einschreiben*
to repair, 32/33	*réparer*	*arreglar*	*riparare*	*reparieren*

	F	S	I	G
restaurant, 26	*le restaurant*	*el restaurante*	*il ristorante*	*das Restaurant(s)*
restaurant guide, 43	*le guide des restaurants*	*la guía de restaurantes*	*la guida dei ristoranti*	*der Restaurantführer(-)*
reverse charge call, 24	*l'appel en PCV (m)*	*la llamada a cobro revertido*	*la chiamata a carico del destinatario*	*das R-Gespräch (e)*
right, 8	*à droite*	*derecha*	*destro/destra*	*rechts*
river, 9	*la rivière*	*el río*	*il fiume*	*der Fluß (Flüsse)*
road, 9	*la route*	*la carretera*	*la strada*	*die Straße(n)*
room, 16/17	*la chambre*	*la habitación*	*la camera*	*das Zimmer(-)*
roundabout, 9	*le rond-point*	*la glorieta*	*la rotonda*	*der Kreisverkehr, der Kreisel*
rubbish bag, 21	*le sac poubelle*	*la bolsa de basura*	*il sacchetto della spazzatura*	*der Müllsack(¨e)*
salad, 29	*la salade*	*la ensalada*	*l'insalata*	*der Salat(e)*
sanitary towels, 35	*les serviettes hygiéniques (f)*	*las compresas*	*gli assorbenti*	*die Binden (f pl)*
to say	*dire*	*decir*	*dire*	*sagen*
to say again, repeat, 4/5	*répéter*	*repetir*	*ripetere*	*etwas noch einmal sagen*
school, 41	*l'école (f)*	*el colegio, la escuela*	*la scuola*	*die Schule(n)*
second, 8	*deuxième*	*segundo/ segunda*	*secondo/ seconda*	*zweite*
to see	*voir*	*ver*	*vedere*	*sehen*
self-service	*le self-service*	*el autoservicio*	*il self-service*	*die Selbstbedienung*
to sell	*vendre*	*vender*	*vendere*	*verkaufen*
to serve, 26/27	*servir*	*servir*	*servire*	*servieren*
shampoo, 35	*le shampooing*	*el champú*	*lo shampoo*	*das Shampoo(s)*
shaving foam, 35	*la crème à raser*	*la espuma de afeitar*	*la schiuma da barba*	*der Rasierschaum*
shopping centre, 32	*le centre commercial*	*el centro comercial*	*il centro*	*das Einkaufszentrum*
shops, 32/33	*les magasins (m)*	*las tiendas*	*i negozi*	*die Läden (m pl), die Geschäfte (n)*
to show, 6/7	*montrer*	*indicar*	*mostrare*	*zeigen*
shower, 18, 20/21	*la douche*	*la ducha*	*la doccia*	*die Dusche(n)*
Shut up!, 54/55	*La ferme!**	*¡Cállate!*	*Sta zitto/zitta!*	*Halt den Mund!**
sign, 8/9	*le panneau*	*la señal*	*l'indicazione (f)*	*das Schild(er)*
Sir, 4	*Monsieur*	*señor*	*Signore*	*Herr*
sister	*la soeur*	*la hermana*	*la sorella*	*die Schwester(n)*
to sit, 26/27	*s'asseoir*	*sentar*	*sedere*	*sitzen*
ski equipment, 46/47				
sleeping bag, 21	*le sac de couchage*	*el saco de dormir*	*il sacco a pelo*	*der Schlafsack(¨e)*
small, 37	*petit/petite*	*pequeño/ pequeña*	*piccolo/piccola*	*klein*
to smoke	*fumer*	*fumar*	*fumare*	*rauchen*

*slang.

	F	S	I	G
soap, 35	*le savon*	*el jabón*	*il sapone*	*die Seife(n)*
something	*quelque chose*	*algo*	*qualche cosa*	*etwas*
Spanish, 40	*l'espagnol (m)*	*el español*	*il spagnolo*	*das Spanisch*
to speak, 4/5, 24/25	*parler*	*hablar*	*parlare*	*sprechen*
sport, 44/45	*le sport*	*el deporte*	*lo sport*	*der Sport*
sports centre, 45	*le centre sportif*	*el centro de deportes*	*il centro sportivo*	*das Sportzentrum (zentren)*
sports equipment, 46/47				
square, 8	*la place, le square*	*la plaza*	*la piazza*	*der Platz(¨e)*
standby, 61	*sans garantie*	*lista de espera*	*lista d'attesa*	*Standby*
starter, 27	*l'entrée (f)*	*el primer plato*	*l'antipasto*	*die Vorspeise(n)*
to stay, 16/17	*rester*	*quedar, estar*	*fermarsi, stare*	*bleiben, wohnen*
to steal, 58	*voler*	*robar*	*rubare*	*stehlen*
stomach ache, 57	*mal au ventre*	*el dolor de estómago*	*il mal di stomaco*	*die Bauchschmerzen (pl)*
to stop, 12/13	*arrêter*	*parar*	*fermare*	*anhalten*
street, 9	*la rue, le boulevard*	*la calle*	*la strada*	*die Straße(n)*
student	*l'étudiant/ l'étudiante*	*el/la estudiante*	*lo studente, la studentessa*	*der Student(en)/ die Studentin(nen)*
student fare, 11	*le tarif étudiant*	*la tarifa de estudiante*	*la tariffa studenti*	*die Studentenermäßigung (en)*
to study, 40/41	*étudier*	*estudiar*	*studiare*	*studieren*
subjects (school), 40	*les matières (f pl)*	*las asignaturas*	*le materie*	*die Fächer (n pl)*
subway, 9	*le passage souterrain*	*el paso subterráneo*	*il sottopassaggio*	*die Unterführung(en)*
sugar, 30	*le sucre*	*el azúcar*	*lo zucchero*	*der Zucker*
suitcase, 59	*la valise*	*la maleta*	*la valigia*	*der Koffer(-)*
sunblock, 34	*l'écran total (m)*	*la crema con protección total*	*la crema con/ schermo solare*	*das Sonnenschutzmittel (-)*
sun-tan lotion, 34	*la crème solaire*	*la crema bronceadora*	*la crema abbronzante*	*die Sonnencreme(s)*
supermarket, 7, 32	*le supermarché, le libre-service*	*el super, el supermercado*	*il supermercato*	*der Supermarkt(¨e)*
swimming pool, 45	*la piscine*	*la piscina*	*la piscina*	*das Schwimmbad (¨er)*
to take, 8/9	*prendre*	*tomar*	*prendere*	*nehmen*
tampons, 35	*les tampons (m pl)*	*los tampones (pl)*	*i tamponi*	*die Tampons (m pl)*
tap water, 20/21	*l'eau du robinet*	*el agua del grifo*	*l'acqua del rubinetto*	*das Leitungswasser*
taxi, 12/13	*le taxi*	*el taxi*	*il tassì*	*das Taxi(s)*
tea, 27	*le thé*	*el té*	*il thè*	*der Tee*

	F	S	I	G
teacher, 41	*le professeur, le/la prof*	*el maestro/ la maestra*	*l'insegnante (m/f)*	*der Lehrer(-), die Lehrerin(nen)*
telephone, 24	*le téléphone*	*el teléfono*	*il telefono*	*das Telefon(e)*
telephone box, 7,24	*la cabine téléphonique*	*la cabina de teléfono*	*la cabina telefonica*	*die Tele- fonzelle(n)*
to tell	*dire*	*decir*	*dire*	*sagen*
tent, 20	*la tente*	*la tienda*	*la tenda*	*das Zelt(e)*
tent peg, 20	*le piquet*	*la estaquilla*	*il paletto*	*der Hering*
thank you, 5	*merci*	*gracias*	*grazie*	*danke*
theatre, 48	*le théâtre*	*el teatro*	*il teatro*	*das Theater (-)*
there	*là*	*allí*	*là, lì*	*dort*
there is	*il y a*	*hay*	*c'è*	*es gibt*
to think about, 32/33	*réfléchir*	*pensar*	*pensare*	*es sich überlegen*
third, 9	*troisième*	*tercero/tercera*	*terzo/terza*	*dritte*
ticket, 10/11, 48/49	*le billet, le ticket*	*el billete, la entrada*	*il biglietto*	*die Fahrkarte(n), die Karte(n)*
return (ticket), 11	*l'aller et retour (m)*	*el billete de ida y vuelta*	*il biglietto di andata e ritorno*	*die Rückfahrkarte*
single (ticket), 11	*l'aller simple (m)*	*el billete de ida*	*il biglietto di sola andata*	*die einfache Fahrkarte*
ticket office, 10	*le guichet*	*la taquilla de billetes, la ventanilla*	*la biglietteria*	*der Fahrkarten- schalter(-), die Theater- kasse(n)*
time	*le temps*	*el tiempo*	*il tempo*	*die Zeit*
timetable, 11	*l'horaire (m)*	*el horario*	*l'orario*	*der Fahrplan(¨e)*
tip (money)	*le pourboire*	*la propina*	*la mancia*	*das Trinkgeld*
tissues, 35	*les mouchoirs en papier (m pl)*	*los pañuelos de papel*	*i fazzolettini di carta*	*die Papier- taschentücher (n pl)*
today	*aujourd'hui*	*hoy*	*oggi*	*heute*
toilet, 20/21	*les toilettes (f pl), les cabinets (m pl)*	*el lavabo*	*i gabinetti (pl)*	*die Toilette(n)*
toilet paper, 21,35	*le papier hygiénique*	*el papel higiénico*	*la carta igienica*	*das Klopapier*
toilet, public, 7	*les toilettes publiques (f pl)*	*los servicios públicos (pl)*	*i gabinetti pubblici (pl)*	*die öffent- liche(n) Toi- lette(n)*
gents (sign)	*messieurs*	*caballeros*	*omini/ signori*	*Herren, Männer*
ladies (sign)	*dames*	*damas*	*donne/ signore*	*Damen, Frauen*
tomorrow	*demain*	*mañana*	*domani*	*morgen*
tonight	*ce soir*	*esta noche*	*questa strasera*	*heute abend*
toothache, 56	*mal aux dents*	*el dolor de muelas*	*il mal di denti*	*die Zahn- schmerzen (pl)*
toothpaste, 35	*le dentifrice*	*la pasta de dientes*	*il dentifricio*	*die Zahnpasta (pasten)*
torch, 21	*une lampe de poche*	*la linterna*	*la torcia*	*die Taschen- lampe(n)*

	F	S	I	G
tourist office, 43	*le Syndicat d'initiative (SI), l'Office du tourisme (OT) (m)*	*la Oficina de Información y Turismo*	*l'ufficio informazioni (turistiche)*	*das Fremdenverkehrsbüro (s)*
towel, 18	*la serviette*	*la toalla*	*l'asciugamano*	*das Handtuch(¨er)*
town plan, 43	*le plan de la ville*	*el plano de la ciudad*	*la piantina della città*	*der Stadtplan (¨e)*
traffic lights, 9	*les feux (m pl)*	*el semáforo*	*il semaforo*	*die Ampel (n)*
train, 10/11	*le train*	*el tren*	*il treno*	*der Zug (¨e)*
translation, 41	*la traduction*	*la traducción*	*la traduzione*	*das Übersetzung(en)*
travel, 10/11, 12/13, 14/15, 60/61				
to travel	*voyager*	*viajar*	*viaggiare*	*unterwegs sein*
travel agent, 33	*l'agence de tourisme*	*la agencia de viajes*	*l'agenzia turistica*	*das Reisebüro(s)*
traveller's cheques, 22/23	*les traveller's chèques (m)*	*los cheques de viaje (pl)*	*i traveller's cheques*	*die Reiseschecks (m pl)*
to try	*essayer*	*intentar*	*provare*	*versuchen*
to turn, 8	*tourner*	*girar, torcer*	*girare*	*abbiegen*
underground station, 6, 10	*la station de métro*	*la estación de metro*	*la stazione della metropolitana*	*die U-Bahn-Station(en)*
underground train	*le métro*	*el metro*	*la metropolitana*	*die U-Bahn*
to understand, 4/5	*comprendre*	*entender*	*capire*	*verstehen*
university, 41	*l'université (f)*	*la universidad*	*l'università*	*das Universität(en)*
to use, 18/19	*utiliser*	*usar*	*usare*	*benutzen*
vacancy (job), 38/39	*le poste vacant*	*el puesto de vacante*	*il posto di lavora libero*	*die Stelle(n)*
vegetables, 28	*les légumes (m)*	*las verduras*	*le verdura*	*das Gemüse*
vegetarian, 18/19	*végétarien/ végétarienne*	*el vegetariano/ la vegetariana*	*il vegetariano/ la vegetariana*	*der Vegetarier(-)/die Vegetarierin(nen)*
very	*très, vachement**	*muy*	*molto*	*sehr*
village	*le village*	*el pueblo*	*il villaggio*	*das Dorf(¨er)*
vineyard, 42	*le vignoble*	*el viñedo*	*il vigneto*	*der Weinberg(e)*
visa, 60	*le visa*	*el visado*	*il visto*	*das Visum (Visen)*
to wake up, 18/19	*se réveiller*	*despertarse*	*svegliare*	*wecken*
to walk	*marcher*	*pasear, andar*	*camminare*	*(zu Fuß) gehen*
wallet	*le porte-feuille*	*la billetera*	*il portafoglio*	*die Brieftasche*
to want, 10/11	*vouloir*	*querer*	*volere*	*möchten, wollen*
washing machine, 19	*la machine à laver*	*la lavadora*	*la lavatrice*	*die Waschmaschine(n)*

*slang.

	F	S	I	G
washing powder, 35	*la lessive*	*el detergente, el jabón en polvo*	*il detersivo*	*das Waschpulver(-)*
water, 20/21	*l'eau (f)*	*el agua (f)*	*l'acqua*	*das Wasser*
week, 12/13	*la semaine*	*la semana*	*la settimana*	*die Woche(n)*
what	*quoi*	*qué/cómo*	*che cosa*	*was*
What is it/this?	*Qu'est-ce que c'est?*	*¿Qué es esto?*	*Cos'è?*	*Was ist das?*
What time...?, 18/19	*Quelle heure...?*	*¿A qué hora...?*	*Che ora...?*	*Wann...?*
What time is it?	*Quelle heure est-il?*	*¿Qué hora es?*	*Che ora è?*	*Wie spät ist es?*
when	*quand*	*cuándo*	*quando*	*wann*
where, 6/7	*où*	*dónde*	*dove*	*Wo, woher*
white	*blanc/blanche*	*blanco/blanca*	*bianco/bianca*	*weiß*
who, 52/53	*qui*	*quién*	*chi*	*wer*
why	*pourquoi*	*por qué*	*perché*	*warum*
wine, 26	*le vin*	*el vino*	*il vino*	*der Wein(e)*
with	*avec*	*con*	*con*	*mit*
woman	*la femme*	*la mujer*	*la donna*	*die Frau(en)*
to write	*écrire*	*escribir*	*scrivere*	*schreiben*
writing paper, 34	*le papier à lettres*	*el papel de escribir*	*la carta da lettere*	*das Schreib-papier*
wrong number, 25	*le mauvais numéro*	*el número equivocado*	*il numero sbagliato*	*falsch verbunden*
to work (function), 12/13	*marcher*	*funcionar*	*funzionare*	*funktionieren*
year	*l'an (m), l'année (f)*	*el año*	*l'anno*	*das Jahr(e)*
yellow	*jaune*	*amarillo/amarilla*	*giallo/gialla*	*gelb*
yes, 4	*oui*	*sí*	*sì*	*ja*
yesterday	*hier*	*ayer*	*ieri*	*gestern*
youth hostel, 6, 17	*l'auberge de jeunesse (f)*	*el albergue juvenil*	*l'ostello della gioventù*	*die Jugend-herberge(n)*

First published in 1992 by Usborne Publishing Ltd., Usborne House, 83-85 Saffron Hill, London EC1N 8RT, England.

Printed in Spain.